POEMS FROM THE GERMAN

Poems from the German

SELECTED BY HELEN PLOTZ

DRAWINGS BY ISMAR DAVID

Thomas Y. Crowell Company · NEW YORK

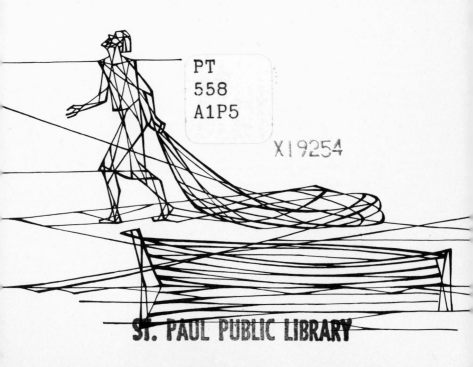

ACKNOWLEDGMENTS

Many friends have helped in the compilation of this book.
Vera Lachmann translated several poems especially for this
volume. Michael Hamburger and Vernon Watkins revised some
of their previous translations. I am especially indebted to Mr.
Hamburger for his generous help in many ways. Norman Buck-
ley and Rebecca Tope coped with all details.

H. P.

*Acknowledgment is made to the following for permission
to reprint copyrighted material.*

ATHENEUM PUBLISHERS for Randall Jarrell's translation of "Die Grosse
Nacht" by Rainer Maria Rilke, made with the permission of Insel-
Verlag, Wiesbaden, from *The Woman at the Washington Zoo*, copyright
© 1960 by Randall Jarrell.

ROBERT BLY for translations of Novalis' "When Geometric Diagrams" and
Hermann Hesse's "Sometimes," published in Volume I, No. 8, The
Sixties Press.

BOLLINGEN FOUNDATION and Stephen Spender for his translation "The
Smith" by Hugo von Hofmannsthal.

EARL V. BROWN, JR., for his translation "Elis" by Georg Trakl, from *The
Harvard Advocate*, March 1966.

THE CITADEL PRESS for Aaron Kramer's translations "Let No Trouble
Overcome You" and "I Dreamed I Had a Lovely Fatherland" by
Heinrich Heine, from *The Poetry and Prose of Heinrich Heine*, pub-
lished 1948.

CITY LIGHTS BOOKS for Jerome Rothenberg's translation "Death Fugue" by
Paul Celan, copyright © 1959 by Jerome Rothenberg.

iv

R. PIPER & CO. VERLAG, Munich, for "Die Gestundete Zeit" by Ingeborg Bachmann, from the volume of the same name published in 1953.

PRINCETON UNIVERSITY PRESS for Edith Abercrombie Snow's translations of "Dream-City of an Emigrant" and "As Your Sweet Ways Enraptured Me to Death" by Franz Werfel, from *Poems*, copyright 1945 by Princeton University Press.

RANDOM HOUSE–ALFRED A. KNOPF, INC., for "Der Einsiedal" and "Vogelshau" and the translations "The Recluse" and "Augury," from *Stefan George: Poems*, translated by Carol North Valhope and Ernst Morwitz, copyright 1943 by Pantheon Books, Inc.

PETER SCHIFFERLI, VERLAGS AG "DIE ARCHE," Zurich, for "Ein Wort," by Gottfried Benn, which appeared originally in the book *Gottfried Benn Statische Gedichte*, 72 pages, Arche-Bucherei Nr. 190/191, copyright by Peter Schifferli, Verlags AG "Die Arche," Zurich.

STEPHEN SPENDER for "Holderlin's Old Age."

CHARLES W. STORK for translation of "The Drunken Song" by Friedrich Nietzsche.

UNIVERSITY OF CALIFORNIA PRESS for Max Knight's translations "Gallows Hill" and "The Aesthetic Weasel" by Christian Morgenstern, from Morgenstern's *Galgenlieder*, published 1963; and for C. F. MacIntyre's translations "Solemn Hour," "Autumn Day," and "The Panther" by Rainer Maria Rilke, from *Selected Poems*, published 1960.

UNIVERSITY OF NORTH CAROLINA PRESS for the following translations by John W. Thomas from *German Verse from the 12th to the 20th Centuries in English Translation*, by John W. Thomas, published 1963: "Lullaby" by Clemens Brentano, "Barbarossa" and "O Stop with Me" by Friedrich Rückert, "Poesie" by Friedrich von Schiller, and "The Broken Ring" by Joseph von Eichendorff.

VERNON WATKINS for his translations "Home" by Friedrich Hölderlin and "The Forsaken Maid" by Eduard Mörike; and for his translation "Many Truly . . ." by Hugo von Hofmannsthal (Pantheon Books).

HARRY ZOHN for his translation "Examination" by Erich Fried.

POEMS OF THE WORLD

Under the editorship of Lillian Morrison

POEMS FROM FRANCE
Selected by William Jay Smith

POEMS FROM THE GERMAN
Selected by Helen Plotz

TABLE OF CONTENTS

INTRODUCTION

Almost the first thing that strikes us when we begin to study the German language is its basic similarity to English. Those English words which come to us either directly from German or from a common source in old Danish or Anglo-Saxon are the words which deal with the fundamental emotions and relations of life. Indeed the word "life" itself, as well as the word "death," comes to us from the same source as the German, as do such simple and meaningful words as "water," "bread," "love" and "hate," "mother" and "father," "brother" and "sister."

This similarity extends in part to German poetry, which in its earliest form resembles the first English lyrics. Dietmar Von Aist's little poem of spring is much like "Sumer is icumen in," the earliest English lyric that we have. Both poets joyously celebrate the greening world and the song of the birds.

The faults of German writing are faults of prose and not of poetry. It is true enough that German prose sentences are unwieldy and needlessly complicated, and true enough that the highly inflected German language itself is hard to manage. Somehow or other, German poets have for the most part avoided the heaviness that usually afflicts German prose. The fact that German lends itself to invented or portmanteau words has been as much an asset to its poetry as it has been a liability to its prose.

In medieval times, the wandering minstrels told the old legends of the German people in castle and cottage. By the twelfth century, the minstrels had become professional

poets. The legends of Parsifal and Tristram and the Nibel-
ungen as we now know them come from this period. The
greatest of poets among the Minnesingers, as the minstrels
once were called, was Walther von der Vogelweide, a poet
who has been called the greatest lyric poet before Goethe.

The folk songs continued to flourish until well into the
seventeenth century. When Martin Luther translated the
Bible into the vernacular, he immeasurably enriched the
German language. The power and simplicity of his style
are most evident in "A Mighty Fortress Is Our God,"
perhaps the greatest of all Christian hymns. "A Mighty
Fortress" stands as a supreme expression of Christian faith.

During the sixteenth and seventeenth centuries, many
other fine hymns and poems were written. By the beginning of the eighteenth century, translations of Shakespeare
and of the Greek classics began to appear. In the middle
of the eighteenth century, the poet and philosopher Johann
Wolfgang von Goethe was born. Classical scholar, scientist,
and political thinker, Goethe combined in his own person
the depths of the classical experience and a romantic
nature-worship. Goethe drew from the literature of all the
world for his inspiration and, in turn, all the world has
come to Goethe. During those years in England, the
romantic poets were experimenting too. Coleridge and
Wordsworth made pilgrimages to Germany. Translations,
both from English to German, as in the famous and excellent Schlegel-Tieck translations of Shakespeare, and
from German to English by Coleridge and later by Longfellow, Bayard Taylor, and Elizabeth Barrett Browning,
began to take root.

Closely associated with Goethe was Friedrich von

Schiller, whose verse dramas so enlarged the German theater. As Bach had done with Luther's hymn, so Beethoven used Schiller's "Hymn to Joy" in his Choral Symphony, and made words and music inseparable.

The earliest of the great romantic poets was Friedrich Hölderlin, born in 1770, the same year as Beethoven and Wordsworth. His concern with Fate, his melancholy, and his love of nature dominated his poems. His recurring images of twilight and of sun and shade are the epitome of romantic poetry, which harks back to the classics in theme rather than in form.

The lovely ballads of Johann Ludwig Uhland are still popular and, like Schiller, he retold many of the old German legends. His most famous poem, "Der Gute Kamerad," was to be tragically echoed by Bertolt Brecht in his "Song of the Storm Trooper" just two hundred years later.

Heinrich Heine was a poet of exile. Some of his finest verse has the ballad qualities which we associate with the romantic movement; it is in fact one of the supreme ironies that when the work of Jews was banned from German schoolbooks, "Die Lorelei" was printed as a folk song. From his self-imposed exile in France, Heine wrote poetry at once despairing, disillusioned, and compassionate. Like the banished poets of Nazi Germany, he never lost his love for his homeland or for his mother tongue.

After Heine and Mörike, there was little great German poetry until Stefan George's verse was published late in the nineteenth century. Like Goethe, George was interested in translation and he translated Shakespeare's sonnets as well as the sonnets of Dante and Petrarch. His experimental forms foreshadowed the expressionist verse of the twentieth century.

Rainer Maria Rilke, born in 1875, is a poet of profoundest spiritual striving. Some of his verse is of Olympic simplicity and some is almost unbelievably complicated. His themes were manifold, for he was concerned with the deepest aspects of life and death, of love and immortality. Unequaled in power and mystery, his verse, as we read and reread it, reveals meaning after meaning. There is much which resists interpretation, and indeed it sometimes seems that Rilke's greatest poems are made from some new language created by an inner struggle immeasurably painful, yet unimaginably joyful.

Early in the twentieth century, a group of poets, painters, and musicians, much influenced by Nietzsche, developed new forms which came to be called "expressionism." The inner anguish felt by such sensitive poets as Georg Trakl and Franz Werfel became the anguish of a disillusioned and defeated people following the First World War. With the rise of Hitler, the artists of Germany were destroyed, suppressed, or exiled. A darkness came on German poetry. It has been said that, after Auschwitz, it would no longer be possible to create a poem. Yet such younger poets as Günter Grass, Paul Celan, and Erich Fried are writing from the depths of the tragic experience of the Nazi years. They even dare to look ahead.

From her exile in Sweden come the poems of Nelly Sachs—who was awarded the Nobel prize for literature in 1966. She is a poet of courage, of hope, and of forgiveness. The everliving voice of German poetry is hers.

POEMS

Wandlung

PLÖTZLICH waren die Kirschen da,
obgleich ich vergessen hatte,
dass es Kirschen gibt
und verkünden liess: Noch nie gab es Kirschen—
waren sie da, plötzlich und teuer.

Pflaumen fielen und trafen mich.
Doch wer da denkt,
ich wandelte mich,
weil etwas fiel und mich traf,
wurde noch nie von fallenden Pflaumen getroffen.

Erst als man Nüsse in meine Schuhe schüttete
und ich laufen musste,
weil die Kinder die Kerne wollten,
schrie ich nach Kirschen, wollt ich von Pflaumen
getroffen werden—und wandelte mich ein wenig.

GÜNTER GRASS
1927–

6

Transformation

SUDDENLY the cherries were there
although I had forgotten
that cherries exist
and caused to be proclaimed:
    There never have been cherries—
they were there, suddenly and dear.

Plums fell and hit me,
but whoever thinks
that I was transformed
because something fell and hit me
has never been hit by falling plums.

Only when they poured nuts into my shoes
and I had to walk
because the children wanted the kernels
I cried out for cherries, wanted plums
to hit me—and was transformed a little.

GÜNTER GRASS
Translated by Michael Hamburger

Nächtliches Stadion

LANGSAM ging der Fussball am Himmel auf.
Nun sah man, dass die Tribüne besetzt war.
Einsam stand der Dichter im Tor,
doch der Schiedsrichter pfiff: Abseits.

GÜNTER GRASS
1927–

Stadium at Night

SLOWLY the football rose in the sky.
Now one could see that the stands were packed.
Alone the poet stood at the goal
but the referee whistled: Off-side.

GÜNTER GRASS
Translated by Michael Hamburger

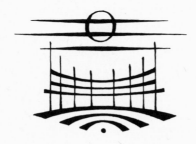

9

Die Gestundete Zeit

Es kommen härtere Tage.
Die auf Widerruf gestundete Zeit
wird sichtbar am Horizont.
Bald musst du den Schuh schnüren
und die Hunde zurückjagen in die Marschhöfe.
Denn die Eingeweide der Fische
sind kalt geworden im Wind.
Ärmlich brennt das Licht der Lupinen.
Dein Blick spurt im Nebel:
die auf Widerruf gestundete Zeit
wird sichtbar am Horizont.
Drüben versinkt dir die Geliebte im Sand,
er steigt um ihr wehendes Haar,
er fällt ihr ins Wort,
er befiehlt ihr zu schweigen,
er findet sie sterblich
und willig dem Abschied
nach jeder Umarmung.
Sieh dich nicht um.
Schnür deinen Schuh.
Jag die Hunde zurück.
Wirf die Fische ins Meer.
Lösch die Lupinen!
Es kommen härtere Tage.

INGEBORG BACHMANN
1926–

The Respite

A HARDER time is coming.
The end of the respite allowed us
appears on the skyline.
Soon you must tie your shoe-lace
and drive back the dogs to the marshland farms.
For the fishes' entrails
have grown cold in the wind.
Poorly the light of the lupins burns.
Your gaze gropes in the fog:
the end of the respite allowed us
appears on the skyline.
Over there your loved one sinks in the sand,
it rises towards her blown hair,
it cuts short her speaking,
it commands her to be silent,
it finds that she is mortal
and willing to part
after every embrace.
Do not look round.
Tie your shoe-lace.
Drive back the dogs.
Throw the fishes into the sea.
Put out the lupins!
A harder time is coming.

INGEBORG BACHMANN
Translated by Michael Hamburger

Todesfuge

SCHWARZE Milch der Frühe wir trinken sie abends
wir trinken sie mittags und morgens wir trinken sie nachts
wir trinken und trinken
wir schaufeln ein Grab in den Lüften da liegt man nicht
    eng

Ein Mann wohnt im Haus der spielt mit den Schlangen
    der schreibt
der schreibt wenn es dunkelt nach Deutschland dein
    goldenes Haar Margarete
er schreibt es und tritt vor das Haus und es blitzen die
    Sterne er pfeift seine Rüden herbei
er pfeift seine Juden hervor lässt schaufeln ein Grab in der
    Erde
er befiehlt uns spielt auf nun zum Tanz

Schwarze Milch der Frühe wir trinken dich nachts
wir trinken dich morgens und mittags wir trinken dich
    abends
wir trinken und trinken

Ein Mann wohnt im Haus und spielt mit den Schlangen
    der schreibt
der schreibt wenn es dunkelt nach Deutschland dein
    goldenes Haar Margarete
Dein aschenes Haar Sulamith wir schaufeln ein Grab in
    den Lüften da liegt man nicht eng

Death Fugue

BLACK milk of morning we drink you at dusktime
we drink you at noontime and dawntime we drink you at
    night
we drink and drink
we scoop out a grave in the sky where it's roomy to lie

There's a man in this house who plays with snakes and
    who writes
who writes when it's nightfall to Germany your
    golden hair Margareta
who writes it and walks from the house and the
stars all start flashing he whistles his dogs to draw near
whistles his Jews to appear starts us scooping a grave out
    of sand
he commands us to play for the dance

Black milk of morning we drink you at night
we drink you at dawntime and noontime we drink you
    at dusktime
we drink and drink

There's a man in this house who plays with snakes and who
    writes
who writes when it's nightfall to Germany your
    golden hair Margareta
your ashen hair Shulamite we scoop out a grave in the sky
    where it's roomy to lie

Er ruft stecht tiefer ins Erdreich ihr einen ihr andern
    singet and spielt
er greift nach dem Eisen im Gurt er schwingts seine Augen
    sind blau
stecht tiefer die Spaten ihr einen ihr andern spielt weiter
    zum Tanz auf

Schwarze Milch der Frühe wir trinken dich nachts
wir trinken dich mittags und morgens wir trinken dich
    abends
wir trinken und trinken
ein Mann wohnt im Haus dein goldenes Haar Margarete
dein aschenes Haar Sulamith er spielt mit den Schlangen

Er ruft spielt süsser den Tod der Tod ist ein Meister aus
    Deutschland
er ruft streicht dunkler die Geigen dann steigt ihr als
    Rauch in die Luft
dann habt ihr ein Grab in den Wolken da liegt man nicht
    eng

Schwarze Milch der Frühe wir trinken dich nachts
wir trinken dich mittags der Tod ist ein Meister aus
    Deutschland
wir trinken dich abends und morgens wir trinken und
    trinken
der Tod ist ein Meister aus Deutschland sein Auge ist blau
er trifft dich mit bleierner Kugel er trifft dich genau

14

[Death Fugue]

He calls jab it deep in the soil you men you other men sing
    and play
he tugs at the sword in his belt he swings it his eyes are
    blue
jab your spades deeper you men you other men play up
    again for the dance

Black milk of morning we drink you at night
we drink you at noontime and dawntime we drink you at
    dusktime
we drink and drink
there's a man in this house your golden hair Margareta
your ashen hair Shulamite he cultivates snakes

He calls play death more sweetly
Death is a master craftsman from Germany
he calls scrape that fiddle more darkly then hover like
    smoke in the air
then scoop out a grave in the clouds where it's roomy
    to lie

Black milk of morning we drink you at night
we drink you at noontime Death is a master craftsman
    from Germany
we drink you at dusktime and dawntime we drink and
    drink
Death is a master craftsman from Germany his eye is blue
he hits you with leaden bullets his aim is true

[Todesfuge]

ein Mann wohnt im Haus dein goldenes Haar Margarete
er hetzt sein Rüden auf uns er schenkt uns ein Grab in
    der Luft
er spielt mit den Schlangen und träumet der Tod ist ein
    Meister aus Deutschland
dein goldenes Haar Margarete
dein aschenes Haar Sulamith

PAUL CELAN
1920–

[Death Fugue]

there's a man in this house your golden hair Margareta
he sets his dogs on our trail he gives us a grave in
    the sky
he plays with snakes and he dreams Death is a master
     craftsman from Germany
your golden hair Margareta
your ashen hair Shulamite

PAUL CELAN
Translated by Jerome Rothenberg

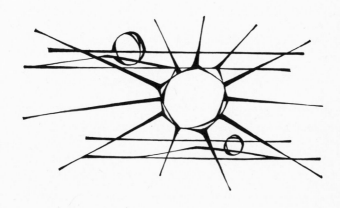

Besichtigung

MAN muss das Unglück
von allen Seiten betrachten

denn von rechts sieht es aus wie Recht
und von links wie Gelingen

und rückwärts wie Rücksicht
und vorne wie Vorteil und Fortschritt

und von oben und unten scheint
es hat Kopf und Fuss

Man muss das Unglück
von allen Seiten betrachten

wenn man dann Glück hat
merkt man es ist das Unglück.

ERICH FRIED
1920—

Examination

ONE must examine misfortune
From all sides.

For from the right it looks so right
And from the left as though left
    especially for us.

Considered from behind it looks like
    considerateness
And from up ahead it feels headily
    like headway.

Viewed from above you can make head
And from below you can make tail of it.

One must examine misfortune
From all sides.

Only then may it be one's good fortune
To recognize that it is misfortune.

ERICH FRIED
Translated by Harry Zohn

Erinnerung an Sonia

IN würziger Wiese
Kniete das schmiegsame Kind.
"Ich mache ein Nest, aus Gras.
Wenn ein Vogel kommt,
Vielleicht zu müde zum Bauen,
Kann er drin wohnen,
Mit seinen Jungen."
Das Licht überglitzerte
Fallendes Dunkelhaar,
Zart gebogenen Nacken,
Schlanken Rückens Geneigtheit,
Trauliche Anmut
Fünfjähriger Mütterlichkeit.

VERA LACHMANN
1904–

Remembering Sonia

In fragrant meadow
Knelt the gentle child.
"I am making a nest with grass—
When a bird comes
Maybe too tired to build,
She can live in it
With her little ones."
The light set sparkling
The falling dark hair,
Tenderly inclined neck,
The bent slender back,
Intimate grace
Of five-year-old motherliness.

VERA LACHMANN
Translated by Spencer Holst

Das Lied vom S. A.-Mann

Als mir der Magen knurrte, schlief ich
Vor Hunger ein.
Da hört ich sie ins Ohr mir
Deutschland erwache! schrein.

Da sah ich viele marschieren
Sie sagten: ins Dritte Reich.
Ich hatte nichts zu verlieren
Und lief mit, wohin war mir gleich.

Als ich marschierte, marschierte
Neben mir ein dicker Bauch
Und als ich "Brot und Arbeit" schrie
Da schrie der Dicke das auch.

Der Stab hatte hohe Stiefel
Ich lief mit nassen Füssen mit
Und wir marschierten beide
In gleichem Schritt und Tritt.

Ich wollte nach links marschieren
Nach rechts marschierte er
Da liess ich mich kommandieren
Und lief blind hinterher.

Und die da Hunger hatten
Marschierten matt und bleich
Zusammen mit den Satten
In irgendein drittes Reich.

Song of the Storm Trooper

FROM hunger I grew drowsy
Dulled by my belly's ache.
Then someone shouted in my ear:
Germany awake!

Then I saw many marching
Toward the Third Reich, they said.
Since I had nought to lose
I followed where they led.

And as I marched, there marched
Big Belly at my side.
When I shouted "Bread and jobs,"
"Bread and jobs," he cried.

The leaders wore high boots,
I stumbled with wet feet.
Yet all of us were marching
To the selfsame beat.

I wanted to march leftward,
Squads right, the order was.
I blindly followed orders
For better or for worse.

And toward some new Third Reich,
But scarcely knowing whither,
Pale and hungry men
And well fed marched together.

[*Das Lied vom S. A.-Mann*]

Sie gaben mir einen Revolver
Und sagten: schiess auf unsern Feind!
Und als ich auf ihren Feind schoss
Da war mein Bruder gemeint.

Jetzt weiss ich: drüben steht mein Bruder.
Der Hunger ists, der uns eint
Und ich marschiere, marschiere
Mit seinem und meinem Feind.

BERTOLT BRECHT
1898–1956

[*Song of the Storm Trooper*]

       They gave me a revolver
       And said: now shoot our foe!
       But as I fired on his ranks
       I laid my brother low.

       It was my brother, hunger
       Made us one I know.
       And I am marching, marching
       With my own and my brother's foe.

BERTOLT BRECHT
Translated by H. R. Hays

25

An Euch, die das neue Haus bauen

[*Aus* IN DEN WOHNUNGEN DES TODES]

WENN du dir deine Wände neu aufrichtest—
Deinen Herd, Schlafstatt, Tisch und Stuhl—
Hänge nicht deine Tränen um sie, die dahingegangen,
Die nicht mehr mit dir wohnen werden
An den Stein
Nicht an das Holz—
Es weint sonst in deinen Schlaf hinein,
Den kurzen, den du noch tun musst.

Seufze nicht, wenn du dein Laken bettest,
Es mischen sich sonst deine Träume
Mit dem Schweiss der Toten.

Ach, es sind die Wände und die Geräte
Wie die Windharfen empfänglich
Und wie ein Acker, darin dein Leid wächst,
Und spüren das Staubverwandte in dir.

Baue, wenn die Stundenuhr rieselt,
Aber weine nicht die Minuten fort
Mit dem Staub zusammen,
Der das Licht verdeckt.

NELLY SACHS
1891–

To You That Build the New House

[*From* THE HABITATIONS OF DEATH]

> *"There are stones like souls"*
> RABBI NACHMAN

WHEN you come to put up your walls anew—
Your stove, your bedstead, table and chair—
Do not hang your tears for those who departed,
Who will not live with you then,
On to the stone.
Nor on the timber—
Else weeping will pierce the sleep
The brief sleep you have yet to take.

Do not sigh when you bed your sheets,
Else your dreams will mingle
With the sweat of the dead.

O, the walls and household utensils
Are responsive as Aeolian harps
Or like a field in which your sorrow grows,
And they sense your kinship with dust.

Build, when the hourglass trickles
But do not weep away the minutes
Together with the dust
That obscures the light.

NELLY SACHS
Translated by Michael Hamburger

27

Welt, frage nicht die Todentrissenen

WELT, frage nicht die Todentrissenen
wohin sie gehen,
sie gehen immer ihrem Grabe zu.
Das Pflaster der fremden Stadt
war nicht für die Musik von Flüchtlingsschritten gelegt
    worden—
Die Fenster der Häuser, die eine Erdenzeit spiegeln
mit den wandernden Gabentischen der Bilderbuch-
    himmel—
wurden nicht für Augen geschliffen,
die den Schrecken an seiner Quelle tranken.
Welt, die Falte ihres Lächelns hat ihnen ein starkes Eisen
    ausgebrannt;
sie möchten so gerne zu dir kommen
um deiner Schönheit wegen,
aber wer heimatlos ist, dem welken alle Wege
wie Schnittblumen hin—

Aber, es ist uns in der Fremde
eine Freundin geworden: die Abendsonne.
Eingesegnet von ihrem Marterlicht
sind wir geladen zu ihr zu kommen mit unserer Trauer,
die neben uns geht:
Ein Psalm der Nacht.

NELLY SACHS
1891–

World Do Not Ask

WORLD do not ask those snatched from death
Where they are going,
They are always going to their graves.
The pavements of the foreign city
Were not laid for the music of fugitive footsteps—
The windows of the houses that reflect a lifetime
Of tables heaped with gifts from a picture-book heaven—
Were not cut for eyes
Which drank terror at its source.
World, a strong iron has cauterized the wrinkle of their
    smile;
They would like to come to you
Because of your beauty,
But for the homeless all ways wither
Like cut flowers—

But we have found a friend
In exile: the evening sun.
Blessed by its suffering-light
We are bidden to come to it with our sorrow
Which walks beside us:
A psalm of night.

NELLY SACHS
Translated by Ruth and Matthew Mead

Als mich dein Wandeln an den Tod verzückte

Als mich dein Dasein tränenwärts entrückte,
Und ich durch dich ins Unermessne schwärmte,
Erlebten diesen Tag nicht Abgehärmte,
Mühselig Millionen Unterdrückte?

Als mich dein Dasein tränenwärts entrückte,
War Arbeit um uns und die Erde lärmte.
Und Leere gab es, gottlos Unerwärmte,
Es lebten und es starben Niebeglückte.

Da ich von dir geschwellt war zum Entschweben,
So viele waren, die im Dumpfen stampften,
An Pulten schrumpften und vor Kesseln dampften.

Ihr Keuchenden auf Strassen und auf Flüssen!
Gibt es ein Gleichgewicht in Welt und Leben,
Wie werd ich diese Schuld bezahlen müssen!?

FRANZ WERFEL
1890–1945

As Your Sweet Ways Enraptured Me to Death

WHILE by your being I was charmed to tears,
And I through you in space soared far away,
Did not unhappy people live that day,
Millions oppressed and wretched all their years?

As your sweet ways enraptured me to death,
The earth was noisy, workers round us trod,
And there were wastes, and folk unwarmed of God.
Men lived and died unblest to their last breath.

As you inspired me till my senses whirled,
There were so many who in darkness fretted,
Crouched over desks and before boilers sweated.

I hear on street and stream their gasping yet!
If there's a balance in this life and world,
In what way will I have to pay this debt?

FRANZ WERFEL
Translated by Edith Abercrombie Snow

Elevation

WELCHEN Weg bist du gegangen
Dass du kamst hier heran?

> Keinen Weg bin ich gegangen.
> Ich sprang ich sprang von Traum zu Traum.

Und du hast dich verirrt nicht
Dort in Fels Wald Schilf Moor?

> Herr, ich nahm doch den Weiser
> Am Kreuzweg den Weiser nicht wahr.

Und es würgten den Fuss dir
Nicht viel Meilen Gestrüpps?

> Ich folg auf dem Sturm her
> Ein Weinen ein einziges Weinen lang.

Sag, was hat dich gerettet
Aus der Sandflut der Nacht?

> Mir im Haar glomm beständig
> Ein Nest ein Nest blauen Lichts.

FRANZ WERFEL
1890–1945

34

Elevation

WHICH way can you have traveled
To have come up this far?

> No way at all it was I traveled.
> I leapt I leapt from dream to dream.

And did you not get lost
There mid crag wood sedge moor?

> The signpost, Lord, at the crossroads,
> I missed the signpost there.

And your feet were not throttled
By undergrowth, mile upon mile?

> I follow hither the storm
> For the fall fall of a single tear.

Tell me, what brought you safely
Through all the nightseas of sand?

> In my hair shone unfailing
> A nest a nest of blue light.

FRANZ WERFEL
Translated by Christopher Middleton

Traumstadt eines Emigranten

JA, ich bin recht, es ist die alte Gasse.
Hier wohn ich dreissig Jahr ohn Unterlass ...
Bin ich hier recht? ? Mich treibt ein Irgendwas,
Das mich nicht loslässt, mit der Menschenmasse.

Da, eine Sperre starrt ... Eh ich mich fasse,
Packt's meine Arme: "Bitte, Ihren Pass!"
Mein Pass? Wo ist mein Pass!? Von Hohn und Hass
Bin ich umzingelt, wanke und erblasse ...

Kann soviel Angst ein Menschenmut ertragen?
Stahlruten pfeifen, die mich werden schlagen,
Ich fühl noch, dass ich in die Kniee brach ...

Und während Unsichtbare mich bespeien:
"Ich hab ja nichts getan," —hör ich mich schreien,
"Als dass ich eure, meine Sprache sprach."

FRANZ WERFEL
1890–1945

Dream-City of an Emigrant

Yes, I am right, it is the well-known street.
I've lived here thirty years without a change . . .
Is this the street? I'm driven by a strange
Compelling force there with the mass to meet.

A barrier looms . . . Before I can retreat
My arm is roughly seized: "Please show your pass!"
My pass? Where is my pass? In a morass
Of scorn and hate I move with faltering feet.

Can human soul endure such anxious fear?
Steel scourges that will strike me whistle near.
The last I know upon my knees I'm flung . . .

And while I'm spat on by an unseen crowd,
"I have done nothing wrong," I scream aloud,
"Except I spoke in your own tongue, *my* tongue."

FRANZ WERFEL
Translated by Edith Abercrombie Snow

Elis

I

VOLLKOMMEN ist die Stille dieses goldenen Tags.
Unter alten Eichen
Erscheinst du, Elis, ein Ruhender mit runden Augen.

Ihre Bläue spiegelt den Schlummer der Liebenden.
An deinem Mund
Verstummten ihre rosigen Seufzer.

Am Abend zog der Fischer die schweren Netze ein.
Ein guter Hirt
Führt seine Herde am Waldsaum hin.
O! wie gerecht sind, Elis, alle deine Tage.

Leise sinkt
An kahlen Mauern des Ölbaums blaue Stille,
Erstirbt eines Greisen dunkler Gesang.

Ein goldener Kahn
Schaukelt, Elis, dein Herz am einsamen Himmel.

II

Ein sanftes Glockenspiel tönt in Elis' Brust
Am Abend,
Da sein Haupt ins schwarze Kissen sinkt.

Ein blaues Wild
Blutet leise im Dornengestrüpp.

Elis

I

FULL is the silence of this golden day.
Under ancient oaks
You appear, Elis, resting with round eyes.

Their blue mirrors the slumber of lovers.
On your mouth
Their rosy sighs went dumb.

At dusk the fisherman hauled in his heavy nets.
A good shepherd
Leads his flocks past the forest's edge.
Oh how just, Elis, are all your days.

Quietly sinks
The olive-trees' blue silence by barren walls,
Dies an old man's dark song.

A golden skiff,
Elis, your heart sways in the lonely sky.

II

A gentle carillon rings in Elis' heart
At dusk,
When he sinks his head in the black pillow.

A blue deer
Bleeds quietly in the briar-patch

[*Elis*]

Ein brauner Baum steht abgeschieden da;
Seine blauen Früchte fielen von ihm.

Zeichen und Sterne
Versinken leise im Abendweiher.

Hinter dem Hügel ist es Winter geworden.

Blaue Tauben
Trinken nachts den eisigen Schweiss,
Der von Elis' kristallener Stirne rinnt.

Immer tönt
An schwarzen Mauern Gottes einsamer Wind.

GEORG TRAKL
1887–1914

[Elis]

A brown tree stands there dead;
The blue fruits have fallen off.

Signs and stars
Sink quietly in the evening pool.

Behind the hill winter has come.

Blue grapes
Drink at night the icy sweat,
That runs from Elis' crystal brow.

Always
God's lonely wind rings by black walls.

GEORG TRAKL
Translated by Earl Brown

Epilog

DIE trunkenen Fluten fallen—
die Stunde des sterbenden Blau
und der erblassten Korallen
um die Insel von Palau.

Die trunkenen Fluten enden
als Fremdes, nicht dein, nicht mein,
sie lassen dir nichts in Händen
als der Bilder schweigendes Sein.

Die Fluten, die Flammen, die Fragen—
und dann auf Asche sehn:
"Leben ist Brückenschlagen
über Ströme, die vergehn."

GOTTFRIED BENN
1886–1956

Epilogue

THE drunken torrents are falling—
the blueness is dying now
and the corals are pale as the water
round the island of Palau.

The drunken torrents are broken,
grown alien, to you, to me,
our only possession the silence
of a bone washed clean by the sea.

The floods, the flames, the questions—
till the ashes tell you one day:
"Life is the building of bridges
over rivers that seep away."

GOTTFRIED BENN
Translated by Michael Hamburger

Ein Wort

Ein Wort, ein Satz—: aus Chiffren steigen
erkanntes Leben, jäher Sinn,
die Sonne steht, die Sphären schweigen
und alles ballt sich zu ihm hin.

Ein Wort—, ein Glanz, ein Flug, ein Feuer,
ein Flammenwurf, ein Sternenstrich—,
und wieder Dunkel, ungeheuer,
im leeren Raum um Welt und Ich.

GOTTFRIED BENN
1886–1956

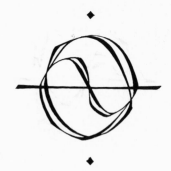

A Word

A WORD, a phrase—; from cyphers rise
Life recognized, a sudden sense,
The sun stands still, mute are the skies,
And all compacts it, stark and dense.

A word—, a gleam, a flight, a spark,
A thrust of flames, a stellar trace—,
And then again—immense—the dark
Round world and I in empty space.

GOTTFRIED BENN
Translated by Richard Exner

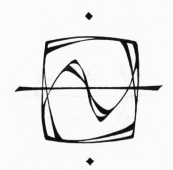

Manchmal

MANCHMAL, wenn ein Vogel ruft
Oder ein Wind geht in den Zweigen
Oder ein Hund bellt im fernsten Gehöft,
Dann muss ich lange lauschen und schweigen.

Meine Seele flieht zurück,
Bis wo vor tausend vergessenen Jahren
Der Vogel und der wehende Wind
Mir ähnlich und meine Brüder waren.

Meine Seele wird ein Baum
Und ein Tier und ein Wolkenweben.
Verwandelt und fremd kehrt sie zurück
Und fragt mich. Wie soll ich Antwort geben?

HERMANN HESSE
1877–1962

Sometimes

SOMETIMES, when a bird cries out,
Or the wind sweeps through a tree,
Or a dog howls in a far off farm,
I hold still and listen a long time.

My soul turns and goes back to the place
Where, a thousand forgotten years ago,
The bird and the blowing wind
Were like me, and were my brothers.

My soul turns into a tree,
And an animal, and a cloud-bank.
Then changed and odd it comes home
And asks me questions. How should I reply?

HERMAN HESSE
Translated by Robert Bly

Aus "Für eine Freundin"

ICH habe Tote, und ich liess sie hin
und war estaunt, sie so getrost zu sehn,
so rasch zuhaus im Totsein, so gerecht,
so anders als ihr Ruf. Nur du, du kehrst
zurück; du streifst mich, du gehst um, du willst
an etwas stossen, dass es klingt von dir
und dich verrät. O nimm mir nicht, was ich
langsam erlern. Ich habe recht; du irrst,
wenn du gerührt zu irgend einem Ding
ein Heimweh hast. Wir wandeln dieses um;
es ist nicht hier, wir spiegeln es herein
aus unserm Sein, sobald wir es erkennen.

RAINER MARIA RILKE
1875–1926

Requiem

[*From* "FOR A FRIEND"]

I HAVE been frequently astonished, letting go
My dead at last, to see them so at home
In death, so unexpectedly at rights,
So in their element that in a trice
'Twas ill to fathom they had ever lived . . .
You only, you come back, and seem to try
To come in touch with something that will ring
Out suddenly, and show that you are here . . .
O rob me not of what I've hardly learnt,
For I am right and you are wrong if still
You covet anything of so-called life.
We change all this, and see there's nothing here
In the clear light of our perfected selves.

RAINER MARIA RILKE
Translated by Hugh MacDiarmid

Für Heide

Sieh mich nicht als Stetes und Erbautes,
weder Brücke kann ich sein, noch Ziel.
Höchstens Mund dem Wagnis eines Lautes,
der mich unbedingter überfiel.

Höchstens Wind in Deinem Blumengrunde,
höchstens weichen Regens Niederfall—,
oder, plötzlich, in der freisten Stunde,
beides: Fangender und Ball.

RAINER MARIA RILKE
1875–1926

For Heather

Do not think of me as built and resting,
goal I am not, bridge I cannot be.
Mouth, at utmost, for a sound's bold testing,
which assaulted more imperiously.

At the utmost, wind in your flower garden,
at the utmost, gentle raindrops' fall—
or, in freest moments, of a sudden,
both: the catcher and the ball.

RAINER MARIA RILKE
Translated by N. K. Cruickshank

Zwölfte Antwort

BEREITES Herz: und wenn ich Dich belüde,
nicht *so*, mit diesem Rohstoff meiner Not;
Du weisst es selber: Unrecht hat, wer müde
zum Leben steht und müder steht zum Tod.

Ich, der ich ausging, beide zu bejahen,
erschrecke vor dem Kampf, der Krankheit heisst;
plötzlich versagt mir an dem Allzunahen
der Raum im Herzen und das Mass im Geist.

Zu solchem Feigesein Dich rufen ... Wie?
Doch komm und schreib mir (Deine Schrift geht leise),
lass Dich in Briefe; von der Frühlingsreise
erzähl dem Freund. Warst Du in Rimini?

RAINER MARIA RILKE
1875–1926

Twelfth Answer

CONSENTING heart: (and if I did not throng you
with all this raw material of distress)
you know yourself, he must be in the wrong who
meets life, and death still more, with weariness.

I, who made praising both my whole career,
faced with the struggle that's called sickness, quail;
all of a sudden for the all-too-near
heart-spaciousness and mental measure fail.

To call you to such cowardice . . . Could I bear?
But come (your pen goes softly) write to me.
Put yourself into letters; tell me where
you went this spring. Were you in Rimini?

RAINER MARIA RILKE
Translated by N. K. Cruickshank

Herbsttag

HERR: es ist Zeit. Der Sommer war sehr gross.
Leg deinen Schatten auf die Sonnenuhren,
und auf den Fluren lass die Winde los.

Befiehl den letzten Früchten voll zu sein;
gib ihnen noch zwei südlichere Tage,
dränge sie zur Vollendung hin und jage
die letzte Süsse in den schweren Wein.

Wer jetzt kein Haus hat, baut sich keines mehr.
Wer jetzt allein ist, wird es lange bleiben,
wird wachen, lesen, lange Briefe schreiben
und wird in den Alleen hin und her
unruhig wandern, wenn die Blätter treiben.

RAINER MARIA RILKE
1875–1926

Die Grosse Nacht

OFT anstaunt ich dich, stand an gestern begonnenem
     Fenster,
stand und staunte dich an. Noch war mir die neue
Stadt wie verwehrt, und die unüberredete Landschaft
finsterte hin, als wäre ich nicht. Nicht gaben die nächsten
Dinge sich Müh, mir verständlich zu sein. An der Laterne

Autumn Day

LORD, it is time. The summer was too long.
Lay now thy shadow over the sundials,
and on the meadows let the winds blow strong.

Bid the last fruit to ripen on the vine;
allow them still two friendly southern days
to bring them to perfection and to force
the final sweetness in the heavy wine.

Who has no house now will not build him one.
Who is alone now will be long alone,
will waken, read, and write long letters
and through the barren pathways up and down
restlessly wander when dead leaves are blown.

RAINER MARIA RILKE
Translated by C. F. MacIntyre

The Great Night

OFTEN I looked at you—stood at the window I had started
The day before, stood and looked at you. The new city still
Seemed something forbidden; the landscape, not yet won
  over,
Darkened as though I was not. The closest things
Didn't bother to make me understand. The street

[*Die Grosse Nacht*]

drängte die Gasse herauf: ich sah, dass sie fremd war.
Drüben ein Zimmer, mitfühlbar, geklärt in der Lampe—,
schon nahm ich teil; sie empfandens, schlossen die Läden.
Stand. Und dann weinte ein Kind. Ich wusste die Mütter
rings in den Häusern, was sie vermögen—, und wusste
alles Weinens zugleich die untröstlichen Gründe.
Oder es sang eine Stimme und reichte ein Stück weit
aus der Erwartung heraus, oder es hustete unten
voller Vorwurf ein Alter, als ob sein Körper im Recht sei
wider die mildere Welt. Dann schlug eine Stunde—,
aber ich zählte zu spät, sie fiel mir vorüber.—
Wie ein Knabe, ein fremder, wenn man endlich ihn zulässt,
doch den Ball nicht fängt und keines der Spiele
kann, die die andern so leicht aneinander betreiben,
dasteht und wegschaut, wohin?—stand ich, und plötzlich,
dass *du* umgehst mit mir, spielest, begriff ich, erwachsene
Nacht, und staunte dich an. Wo die Türme
zürnten, wo abgewendeten Schicksals
eine Stadt mich umstand, und nicht zu erratende Berge
wider mich lagen, und im genäherten Umkreis
hungernde Fremdheit umzog das zufällige Flackern
meiner Gefühle: da war es, du Hohe,
keine Schande für dich, dass du mich kanntest. Dein Atem
ging über mich; dein auf weite Ernste verteiltes
Lächeln trat in mich ein.

RAINER MARIA RILKE
1875–1926

58

[*The Great Night*]

Crowded itself up to the lamp post; I saw that it was strange.
Out there a room was clear in lamplight—
Already I was part; they sensed it, closed the shutters.
I stood there. And then a child cried. And I knew
The mothers in the houses, what they were—knew,
    suddenly,
The spring of all our tears, the spring that is never dry.
Or a voice sang, and went a little beyond
Whatever I had expected; or an old man coughed,
Full of reproach, as though his flesh were in the right
Against the gentler world. Then a clock struck the hour—
But I counted too late, and it got by me.
As a boy, a stranger, when at last they let him,
Can't catch the ball, and doesn't know any of the games
The others are playing together so easily,
So that he stands and looks off—where?—I stand, and
    suddenly
See that *you* have made friends with me, played with me,
    grown-up
Night, and I look at you. While the towers
Were angered, while with averted fates
A city encompassed me, and the unguessable hills
Were encamped against me, and in closing circles
Strangeness hungered round the chance-set flares
of my senses: then was it, O highest,
That you felt it no shame to know me, that your breath
Went over me, that there passed into me
Your grave and from far apportioning smile.

RAINER MARIA RILKE
Translated by Randall Jarrell

59

Ernste Stunde

WER jetzt weint irgendwo in der Welt,
ohne Grund weint in der Welt,
weint über mich.

Wer jetzt lacht irgendwo in der Nacht,
ohne Grund lacht in der Nacht,
lacht mich aus.

Wer jetzt geht irgendwo in der Welt,
ohne Grund geht in der Welt,
geht zu mir.

Wer jetzt stirbt irgendwo in der Welt,
ohne Grund stirbt in der Welt,
sieht mich an.

RAINER MARIA RILKE
1875–1926

Solemn Hour

Who weeps now anywhere in the world,
without cause weeps in the world,
weeps over me.

Who laughs now anywhere in the night,
without cause laughs in the night,
laughs at me.

Who goes now anywhere in the world,
without cause goes in the world,
goes to me.

Who dies now anywhere in the world,
without cause dies in the world,
looks at me.

RAINER MARIA RILKE
Translated by C. F. MacIntyre

Der Panther

Im *Jardin des Plantes, Paris*

SEIN Blick ist vom Vorübergehn der Stäbe
So müd geworden, dass er nichts mehr hält.
Ihm ist, als ob es tausend Stäbe gäbe
und hinter tausend Stäben keine Welt.

Der weiche Gang geschmeidig starker Schritte,
der sich im allerkleinsten Kreise dreht,
ist wie ein Tanz von Kraft um eine Mitte,
in der betäubt ein grosser Wille steht.

Nur manchmal schiebt der Vorhang der Pupille
sich lautlos auf—. Dann geht ein Bild hinein,
geht durch der Glieder angespannte Stille—
und hört im Herzen auf zu sein.

RAINER MARIA RILKE
1875–1926

The Panther

Jardin des Plantes, Paris

His sight from ever gazing through the bars
has grown so blunt that it sees nothing more.
It seems to him that thousands of bars are
before him, and behind them nothing merely.

The easy motion of his supple stride,
which turns about the very smallest circle,
is like a dance of strength about a center
in which a mighty will stands stupefied.

Only sometimes when the pupil's film
soundlessly opens . . . then one image fills
and glides through the quiet tension of the limbs
into the heart and ceases and is still.

RAINER MARIA RILKE
Translated by C. F. MacIntyre

1. Teil, Sonett 18

[*Aus* SONETTE AN ORPHEUS]

HÖRST du das Neue, Herr,
dröhnen und beben?
Kommen Verkündiger,
die es erheben.

Zwar ist kein Hören heil
in dem Durchtobtsein,
doch der Maschinenteil
will jetzt gelobt sein.

Sieh, die Maschine:
wie sie sich wälzt und rächt
und uns entstellt und schwächt.

Hat sie aus uns auch Kraft,
sie, ohne Leidenschaft,
treibe und diene.

RAINER MARIA RILKE
1875–1926

Part 1—Sonnet 18

[*From* SONNETS TO ORPHEUS]

LORD, do you hear it there,
throbbing and humming?
Prophets with zeal declare
new things are coming.

What though no ear be hale,
clangours so daze it?
Let the machine prevail;
ours but to praise it.

Machine, pound away,
blemish and slacken us,
get your own back on us.

Though you partake our strength,
you shall be tamed at length,
drive and obey.

RAINER MARIA RILKE
Translated by Eudo C. Mason

Der Schmied

[*Aus* IDYLLE]

DIE ganze kenn ich, kennend meinen Kreis,
Massloses nicht verlangend, noch begierig ich,
Die flüchtge Flut zu ballen in der hohlen Hand.
Den Bach, der deine Wiege schaukelte, erkennen lern,
Den Nachbarbaum, der dir die Früchte an der Sonne reift
Und dufterfüllten lauen Schatten niedergiesst,
Das kühle grüne Gras, es trats dein Fuss als Kind.
Die alten Eltern tratens, leise frierende,
Und die Geliebte trats, da quollen duftend auf
Die Veilchen, schmiegend unter ihre Sohlen sich;
Das Haus begreif, in dem du lebst und sterben sollst,
Und dann, ein Wirkender, begreif dich selber
  ehrfurchtsvoll,
An diesen hast du mehr, als du erfassen kannst—

HUGO VON HOFMANNSTHAL
1874–1929

The Smith

[*From* IDYLL]

I KNOW the whole in knowing my own boundaries,
Not yearning for the immeasurable, nor ever seeking
To clench the fleeting flood within my hollow hand.
The stream which rocked your cradle, that learn to know,
The nearby tree ripening fruit for you in the sun,
Casting down lukewarm shadows heavy with fragrance,
The cool green grass your foot trod when you were a child.
Your aged parents trod it, shivering slightly,
And the beloved one trod it: fragrant, there swelled up
The violet, meekly bending under their soles.
Grasp the one house in which you must live and die,
And then, as one accomplishing, grasp your own self
    with awe;
These things alone are more than ever you'll comprehend.

HUGO VON HOFMANNSTHAL
Translated by Stephen Spender

Manche freilich . . .

MANCHE freilich müssen drunten sterben,
Wo die schweren Ruder der Schiffe streifen,
Andre wohnen bei dem Steuer droben,
Kennen Vogelflug und die Länder der Sterne.

Manche liegen immer mit schweren Gliedern
Bei den Wurzeln des verworrenen Lebens,
Andern sind die Stühle gerichtet
Bei den Sibyllen, den Königinnen,
Und da sitzen sie wie zu Hause,
Leichten Hauptes und leichter Hände.

Doch ein Schatten fällt von jenen Leben
In die anderen Leben hinüber,
Und die leichten sind an die schweren
Wie an Luft und Erde gebunden:

Ganz vergessener Völker Müdigkeiten
Kann ich nicht abtun von meinen Lidern,
Noch weghalten von der erschrockenen Seele
Stummes Niederfallen ferner Sterne.

Viele Geschicke weben neben dem meinen,
Durcheinander spielt sie alle das Dasein,
Und mein Teil ist mehr als dieses Lebens
Schlanke Flamme oder schmale Leier.

HUGO VON HOFMANNSTHAL
1874–1929

Many Truly...

MANY truly down below must perish
Where the heavy oars of ships are passing;
Others by the helm up there have dwelling,
Know the flight of birds and starry countries.

Many lie with heavy limbs remaining
Near the roots of life obscurely tangled;
There are chairs meanwhile set up for others
Near to sibyls, queens for their companions,
And they sit there as at home contented,
Easy in their heads, in their hands easy.

Yet from their existence falls a shadow
Reaching the existence of those others,
And the easy are to the burdened
Bound, as to earth and air, together.

I can never cast off from my eyelids
Lassitudes of long-forgotten peoples,
Nor from my astounded soul can banish
Soundless fall of stars through outer distance.

Many destinies with mine are woven;
Living plays them all through one another,
And my part is larger than this slender
Life's ascending flame or narrow lyre.

HUGO VON HOFMANNSTHAL
Translated by Vernon Watkins

Der Aesthetische Wiesel

EIN Wiesel
sass auf einem Kiesel
inmitten Bachgeriesel.

Wisst ihr
weshalb?

Das Mondkalb
verriet es mir
im Stillen:

Das raffinier—
te Tier
tat's um des Reimes willen.

CHRISTIAN MORGENSTERN
1871–1914

The Aesthetic Weasel

A WEASEL
perched on an easel
within a patch of teasel.

But why
and how?

The Moon Cow
whispered her reply
one time:

The sopheest-
icated beest
just did it for the rhyme.

CHRISTIAN MORGENSTERN
Translated by Max Knight

Vice Versa

Ein Hase sitzt auf einer Wiese,
des Glaubens, niemand sähe diese.

Doch, im Besitze eines Zeisses,
betrachtet voll gehaltnen Fleisses

vom vis-à-vis gelegnen Berg
ein Mensch den kleinen Löffelzwerg.

Ihn aber blickt hinwiederum
ein Gott von fern an, mild und stumm.

CHRISTIAN MORGENSTERN
1871–1914

Vice Versa

THE rabbit sits upon the green
In the belief it is unseen.

Yet from a neighboring mountain slope
A huntsman with a telescope

Observes the little beast with tense
And silent-watching diligence.

Him also from the distant sky
God holds in his all-seeing eye.

CHRISTIAN MORGENSTERN
Translated by R. F. C. Hull

Galgenberg

BLÖDEM Volke unverständlich
treiben wir des Lebens Spiel.
Grade das, was unabwendlich
fruchtet unserm Spott als Ziel.

Magst es Kinder-Rache nennen
an des Daseins tiefem Ernst;
wirst das Leben besser kennen,
wenn du uns verstehen lernst.

CHRISTIAN MORGENSTERN
1871–1914

Gallows Hill

ENIGMATIC for the masses
playfully with life we fool.
That which human wits surpasses
draws our special ridicule.

Call it infantile vendetta
on life's deeply serious aim—
you will know existence better
once you understand our game.

CHRISTIAN MORGENSTERN
Translated by Max Knight

Mein Volk

Der Fels wird morsch,
Dem ich entspringe
Und meine Gotteslieder singe . . .
Jäh stürz ich vom Weg
Und riesele ganz in mir
Fernab, allein über Klagegestein
Dem Meer zu.

Hab mich so abgeströmt
Von meines Blutes
Mostvergorenheit.
Und immer, immer noch der Widerhall
In mir,
Wenn schauerlich gen Ost
Das morsche Felsgebein,
Mein Volk,
Zu Gott schreit.

ELSE LASKER-SCHÜLER
1869–1945

My People

THE rock grows brittle
From which I spring
To which my canticles I sing . . .
Down I rush from the track
And inwardly only ripple
Far off, alone over wailing stones
Toward the sea.

Have flowed so much away
From the wine ferment
Of my blood.
And yet for ever, endlessly the echo
In me,
When eastward, awesomely,
The brittle rock of bone,
My people,
Cries out to God.

ELSE LASKER-SCHÜLER
Translated by Michael Hamburger

Vogelschau

Weisse schwalben sah ich fliegen,
Schwalben schnee- und silberweiss,
Sah sie sich im winde wiegen,
In dem winde hell und heiss.

Bunte häher sah ich hüpfen,
Papagei und kolibri
Durch die wunder-bäume schlüpfen
In dem wald der Tusferi.

Grosse raben sah ich flattern,
Dohlen schwarz und dunkelgrau
Nah am grunde über nattern
Im verzauberten gehau.

Schwalben seh ich wieder fliegen,
Schnee- und silberweisse schar,
Wie sie sich im winde wiegen
In dem winde kalt und klar!

STEFAN GEORGE
1868–1933

Augury

WHITE I saw the swallows winging,
Swallows snow- and silver-white,
In the wind I saw them clinging,
In the burning wind and bright.

Jays I saw that slipped and shimmered,
Parakeet and colibri
Through the trees of wonder glimmered,
In the wood of Tusferi.

Huge I saw the ravens slacken,
Daws of black and sombre grey,
Over adders, near the bracken,
Where the magic timber lay.

Now again I see the winging
Snow and silver swallows veer,
In the wind I see them clinging,
In the freezing wind and clear!

STEFAN GEORGE
*Translated by Carol North Valhope
and Ernst Morwitz*

Der Einsiedel

INS offne fenster nickten die hollunder
Die ersten reben standen in der bluht,
Da kam mein sohn zurück vom land der wunder,
Da hat mein sohn an meiner brust geruht.

Ich liess mir allen seinen kummer beichten,
Gekränkten stolz auf seinem erden-ziehn—
Ich hätte ihm so gerne meinen leichten
Und sichern frieden hier bei mir verliehn.

Doch anders fügten es der himmel sorgen—
Sie nahmen nicht mein reiches lösegeld . . .
Er ging an einem jungen ruhmes-morgen,
Ich sah nur fern noch seinen schild im feld.

STEFAN GEORGE
1868–1933

The Recluse

THE elders through the open window swayed,
The vines already into blossom pressed,
Then home my son from lands of wonder strayed,
My son then lay at rest upon my breast.

I let him tell the tale of all his woe,
In earthly farings all his wounded pride—
I should have liked so much to have him know
The calm and poised secureness at my side.

But other goals the cares of heaven frame—
Though rich my ransom, they refused to yield . . .
He left upon a morning young with fame,
I watched his shield move through the distant field.

STEFAN GEORGE
*Translated by Carol North Valhope
and Ernst Morwitz*

Das Trunkene Lied

O MENSCH! Gib acht!
Was spricht die tiefe Mitternacht?
"Ich schlief, ich schlief—,
Aus tiefem Traum bin ich erwacht:—
Die Welt ist tief,
Und tiefer als der Tag gedacht.
Tief ist ihr Weh—,
Lust—tiefer noch als Herzeleid:
Weh spricht: Vergeh!
Doch alle Lust will Ewigkeit—,
—Will tiefe, tiefe Ewigkeit!"

FRIEDRICH NIETZSCHE
1844–1900

The Drunken Song

O MAN, what seem
The words, that from deep Midnight stream?
"I was asleep—
I have awakened from my dream.
The world is deep,
Yea, deeper far than Day could deem.
Deep is your grief,
But deeper Joy than Grief can be.
'Life, be thou brief!' sighs Grief.
But Joy would have Eternity—
Would have deep, deep Eternity."

FRIEDRICH NIETZSCHE
Translated by Charles W. Stork

Das verlassene Mägdlein

FRÜH, wann die Hähne krähn,
Eh' die Sternlein verschwinden,
Muss ich am Herde stehn,
Muss Feuer zünden.

Schön ist der Flammen Schein,
Es springen die Funken;
Ich schaue so drein,
In Leid versunken.

Plötzlich, da kommt es mir,
Treuloser Knabe,
Dass ich die Nacht von dir
Geträumet habe.

Träne auf Träne dann
Stürzet hernieder;
So kommt der Tag heran—
O ging' er wieder!

EDUARD MÖRIKE
1804–1875

The Forsaken Maid

EARLY, when first cocks crow,
Before the stars fade,
I to the hearth must go;
Fire must be made.

Fair is the flames' bright light,
The sparks fly dancing;
Gazing, I see my plight
Held there entrancing.

Sudden it comes to me,
Boy so untrue,
That, as the night went by,
I dreamed of you.

Tear, then, on tear runs down,
Constantly flowing.
So comes the new day on—
O, were it going!

EDUARD MÖRIKE
Translated by Vernon Watkins

Frage

O Menschenherz, was ist dein Glück?
Ein rätselhaft geborner
Und, kaum gegrüsst, verlorner,
Unwiederholter Augenblick!

NIKOLAUS LENAU
1802–1850

In der Fremde

ICH hatte einst ein schönes Vaterland.
Der Eichenbaum
Wuchs dort so hoch, die Veilchen nickten sanft.
Es war ein Traum.

Das küsste mich auf deutsch, und sprach auf deutsch
(Man glaubt es kaum
Wie gut es klang) das Wort: "Ich liebe dich!"
Es war ein Traum.

HEINRICH HEINE
1802–1850

Question

WHAT is thy joy, O heart of man?
Delight uncomprehended;
When hardly welcomed, ended;
One unreturning moment's span.

NIKOLAUS LENAU
Translated by Dwight Durling

I Dreamed I Had
a Lovely Fatherland

I DREAMED I had a lovely fatherland.
The sturdy oak
Grew tall there, and the violets gently swayed.
Then I awoke.

I dreamed a German kiss was on my brow.
And someone spoke
The German words: "I love you!" (How they rang!)
Then I awoke.

HEINRICH HEINE
Translated by Aaron Kramer

Mein Kind, wir waren Kinder

MEIN Kind, wir waren Kinder,
Zwei Kinder, klein und froh;
Wir krochen ins Hühnerhäuschen,
Versteckten uns unter das Stroh.

Wir krähten wie die Hähne,
Und kamen Leute vorbei—
"Kikeriki!" sie glaubten,
Es wäre Hahnengeschrei.

Die Kisten auf unserem Hofe,
Die tapezierten wir aus,
Und wohnten drin beisammen,
Und machten ein vornehmes Haus.

Des Nachbars alte Katze
Kam öfters zum Besuch;
Wir machten ihr Bückling' und Knickse
Und Komplimente genug.

Wir haben nach ihrem Befinden
Besorglich und freundlich gefragt;
Wir haben seitdem dasselbe
Mancher alten Katze gesagt.

Wir sassen auch oft und sprachen
Vernünftig wie alte Leut'
Und klagten, wie alles besser
Gewesen zu unserer Zeit,

My Child, We Were Two Children

My child, we were two children,
Small, merry by childhood's law;
We used to creep to the henhouse,
And hide ourselves in the straw.

We crowed like cocks, and whenever
The passers near us drew—
"Cock-a-doodle!" they thought
'Twas a real cock that crew.

The boxes about our courtyard
We carpeted to our mind,
And lived there both together—
Kept house in a noble kind.

The neighbor's old cat often
Came to pay us a visit;
(We have made the very same speeches
Each with a compliment in it.)

After her health we asked,
Our care and regard to evince—
(We have made the very same speeches
To many an old cat since.)

We also sat and wisely
Discoursed, as old folks do,
Complaining how all went better
In those good old times we knew;—

[*Mein Kind, wir waren Kinder*]

Wie Lieb' und Treu' und Glauben
Verschwunden aus der Welt,
Und wie so teuer der Kaffee,
Und wie so rar das Geld!—

Vorbei sind die Kinderspiele,
Und alles rollt vorbei—
Das Geld und die Welt und die Zeiten,
Und Glauben und Lieb' und Treu'.

HEINRICH HEINE
1797–1856

Herz, mein Herz, sei nicht beklommen

HERZ, mein Herz, sei nicht beklommen
Und ertrage dein Geschick.
Neuer Frühling gibt zurück,
Was der Winter dir genommen.

Und wie viel ist dir geblieben,
Und wie schön ist noch die Welt!
Und mein Herz, was dir gefällt,
Alles, alles darfst du lieben!

HEINRICH HEINE
1797–1856

[My Child, We Were Two Children]

How love, and truth, and believing
Had left the world to itself,
And how so dear was the coffee,
And how so rare was the pelf.

The children's games are over,
The rest is over with youth—
The world, the good games, the good times,
The belief, and the love, and the truth.

HEINRICH HEINE
Translated by
Elizabeth Barrett Browning

Let No Trouble Overcome You

LET no trouble overcome you,
Heart, my heart—but bear your pain.
Spring shall come, and bring again
All that Winter's taken from you.

And how great is still your treasure!
And the world, how fair a place!
And, my heart, you may embrace
All on earth that gives you pleasure.

HEINRICH HEINE
Translated by Aaron Kramer

Lorelei

Ich weiss nicht, was soll es bedeuten,
Dass ich so traurig bin;
Ein Märchen aus alten Zeiten,
Das kommt mir nicht aus dem Sinn.

Die Luft ist kühl, und es dunkelt,
Und ruhig fliesst der Rhein;
Der Gipfel des Berges funkelt
Im Abendsonnenschein.

Die schönste Jungfrau sitzet
Dort oben wunderbar,
Ihr goldnes Geschmeide blitzet,
Sie kämmt ihr goldenes Haar.

Sie kämmt es mit goldenem Kamme
Und singt ein Lied dabei;
Das hat eine wundersame,
Gewaltige Melodei.

Den Schiffer im kleinen Schiffe
Ergreift es mit wildem Weh;
Er schaut nicht die Felsenriffe,
Er schaut nur hinauf in die Höh!

Lorelei

I CANNA tell what has come ower me
    That I am sae eerie and wae;
An auld-warld tale comes before me,
    It haunts me by nicht and by day.

From the cool lift the gloamin' draps dimmer,
    And the Rhine slips saftly by;
The taps of the mountains shimmer
    I' the lowe o' the sunset sky.

Up there, in a glamor entrancin',
    Sits a maiden wondrous fair;
Her gowden adornments are glancing,
    She is kaimin' her gowden hair.

As she kaims it the gowd kaim glistens,
    That while she is singin' a song
That hauds the rapt soul that listens,
    With its melody sweet and strong.

The boy, floating by in vague wonder,
    Is seized with a wild weird love;
He sees na the black rocks under,—
    He sees but the vision above.

Ich glaube, die Wellen verschlingen
Am Ende Schiffer und Kahn;
Und das hat mit ihrem Singen
Die Lorelei getan.

HEINRICH HEINE
1797–1856

Der Weiher

Er liegt so still im Morgenlicht,
So friedlich wie ein fromm Gewissen.
Wenn Weste seine Spiegel küssen,
Des Ufers Blume fühlt es nicht;
Libellen zittern über ihn,
Blaugoldne Stäbchen und Karmin,
Und auf des Sonnenbildes Glanz
Die Wasserspinne führt den Tanz.
Schwertlilienkranz am Ufer steht
Und horcht des Schilfes Schlummerliede,
Ein lindes Säuseln kommt und geht,
Als flüstr'es: Friede! Friede! Friede!

ANNETTE VON DROSTE-HÜLSHOFF
1797–1848

[*Lorelei*]

The water their waves are flingin'
    Ower boatie and boatman anon;
And this, with her airtful singin',
    The Waterwitch Lurley hath done.

HEINRICH HEINE
Translated by Alexander Macmillan

The Pond

IT lies so still in morning's gleam,
As peaceful as a conscience shriven.
Wind-kisses, to its mirror given,
Don't stir the framing flowers' dream.
Above it dragon-flies are trembling,
Bluegold and carmine wands resembling;
A water-spider weaves its dance
On glittering sun-reflection's glance.
Ashore, a wreath of iris grows.
The rushes' lulling does not cease.
A gentle shiver comes and goes,
As if it whispered: Peace! Peace! Peace!

ANNETTE VON DROSTE-HÜLSHOFF
Translated by Vera Lachmann

97

Kehr ein bei mir!

Du bist die Ruh,
Der Friede mild,
Die Sehnsucht du,
Und was sie stillt.

Ich weihe dir
Voll Lust und Schmerz
Zur Wohnung hier
Mein Aug' und Herz.

Kehr ein bei mir
Und schliesse du
Still hinter dir
Die Pforten zu!

Treib andern Schmerz
Aus dieser Brust!
Voll sei dies Herz
Von deiner Lust.

Dies Augenzelt,
Von deinem Glanz
Allein erhellt,
O füll es ganz!

FRIEDRICH RÜCKERT
1788–1866

O Stop with Me

THOU art repose
and quiet calm,
desire that glows
and cooling balm.

I give thee, dear,
with joy and sighs
a dwelling here—
my heart and eyes.

Stop in with me
and be not late,
and after thee
make fast the gate.

Have care depart
from out this breast,
and fill my heart
with love, and rest.

Alone through thee
my eyes have sight;
O let them be
filled with thy light.

FRIEDRICH RÜCKERT
Translated by John W. Thomas

Barbarossa

DER alte Barbarossa,
Der Kaiser Friederich,
Im unterirdschen Schlosse
Hält er verzaubert sich.

Er ist niemals gestorben,
Er lebt darin noch jetzt;
Er hat im Schloss verborgen
Zum Schlaf sich hingesetzt.

Er hat hinabgenommen
Des Reiches Herrlichkeit
Und wird einst wiederkommen
Mit ihr zu seiner Zeit.

Der Stuhl ist elfenbeinern,
Darauf der Kaiser sitzt;
Der Tisch ist marmelsteinern,
Worauf sein Haupt er stützt.

Sein Bart ist nicht von Flachse,
Er ist von Feuersglut,
Ist durch den Tisch gewachsen,
Worauf sein Haupt ausruht.

Er nickt als wie im Traume,
Sein Aug' halb offen zwinkt,
Und je nach langem Raume
Er einem Knaben winkt.

Barbarossa

OLD Friedrich Barbarossa,
the emperor renowned,
inhabits now, enchanted,
a castle underground.

Not dead is he, but resting,
he still lives there today,
and in this hidden castle
he sits and sleeps away.

He took the empire's glory
down with him in its prime,
and will return in splendor
with it, in his own time.

The chair on which he slumbers
of ivory is made,
the table is of marble
on which his head is laid.

His flowing beard, not flaxen
but red with fiery glow,
has grown right through the table
and to the stone below.

He nods and stirs in dreaming
and winks a sleepy eye,
and now and then he beckons
a servant, standing by.

[*Barbarossa*]

Er spricht im Schlaf zum Knaben:
"Geh hin vors Schloss, o Zwerg,
Und sieh, ob noch die Raben
Herfliegen um den Berg.

Und wenn die alten Raben
Noch fliegen immerdar,
So muss ich auch noch schlafen
Verzaubert hundert Jahr."

FRIEDRICH RÜCKERT
1788–1866

[*Barbarossa*]

He speaks to him in slumber:
"Find out, O dwarf, if still
you see the ravens flying
above the castle hill.

And if the ancient ravens
above the castle soar,
then I must sleep, enchanted,
a hundred years or more."

FRIEDRICH RÜCKERT
Translated by John W. Thomas

Das zerbrochene Ringlein

In einem kühlen Grunde
Da geht ein Mühlenrad,
Mein' Liebste ist verschwunden,
Die dort gewohnet hat.

Sie hat mir Treu versprochen,
Gab mir ein'n Ring dabei,
Sie hat die Treu gebrochen,
Mein Ringlein sprang entzwei.

Ich möcht' als Spielmann reisen
Weit in die Welt hinaus
Und singen meine Weisen
Und gehn von Haus zu Haus.

Ich möcht' als Reiter fliegen
Wohl in die blut'ge Schlacht,
Um stille Feuer liegen
Im Feld bei dunkler Nacht.

Hör' ich das Mühlrad gehen:
Ich weiss nicht, was ich will—
Ich möcht' am liebsten sterben,
Da wär's auf einmal still!

JOSEPH VON EICHENDORFF
1798–1857

104

The Broken Ring

BESIDE the shaded water
an ancient mill wheel turns,
but now the miller's daughter
has left those rocks and ferns.

She gave a ring, a token
of pledges to be true;
her promises were broken,
my ring then broke in two.

I would as minstrel wander
the wide world up and down,
and sing my songs out yonder
from town to distant town!

I would with gallant squires
ride to the bloody fight,
and sleep by silent fires
upon the field at night!

I hear the mill wheel turning
and know not what I will.
For death I'm ever longing,
for then it would be still.

JOSEPH VON EICHENDORFF
Translated by John W. Thomas

Das Schloss am Meere

"HAST du das Schloss gesehen,
Das hohe Schloss am Meer?
Golden und rosig wehen
Die Wolken drüber her.

Es möchte sich niederneigen
In die spiegelklare Flut,
Es möchte streben und steigen
In der Abendwolken Glut."—

"Wohl hab' ich es gesehen,
Das hohe Schloss am Meer
Und den Mond darüber stehen
Und Nebel weit umher."—

"Der Wind und des Meeres Wallen,
Gaben sie frischen Klang?
Vernahmst du aus hohen Hallen
Saiten und Festgesang?"—

"Die Winde, die Wogen alle
Lagen in tiefer Ruh;
Einem Klagelied aus der Halle
Hört' ich mit Tränen zu."—

"Sahest du oben gehen
Den König und sein Gemahl?
Der roten Mäntel Wehen,
Der goldnen Kronen Strahl?

The Castle by the Sea

"HAST thou seen that lordly castle,
 That Castle by the Sea?
Golden and red above it
 The clouds float gorgeously.

And fain it would stoop downward
 To the mirrored wave below:
And fain it would soar upward
 In the evening's crimson glow."

"Well have I seen that castle,
 That Castle by the Sea,
And the moon above it standing,
 And the mist rise solemnly."

"The winds and the waves of ocean,
 Had they a merry chime?
Didst thou hear, from those lofty chambers
 The harp and the minstrel's rhyme?"

"The winds and the waves of ocean,
 They rested quietly,
But I heard on the gale a sound of wail,
 And tears came to mine eye."

"And sawest thou on the turrets
 The King and his royal bride?
And the wave of their crimson mantles?
 And the golden crown of pride?

Führten sie nicht mit Wonne
Eine schöne Jungfrau dar,
Herrlich wie eine Sonne,
Strahlend im goldnen Haar?"—

"Wohl sah ich die Eltern beide
Ohne der Kronen Licht,
Im schwarzen Trauerkleide—
Die Jungfrau sah ich nicht."

JOHANN LUDWIG UHLAND
1787–1862

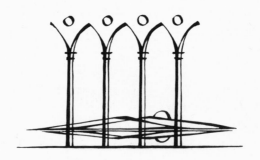

[*The Castle by the Sea*]

    Led they not forth, in rapture,
        A beauteous maiden there?
    Resplendent as the morning sun,
        Beaming with golden hair?"

    "Well saw I the ancient parents,
        Without the crown of pride;
    They were moving slow, in weeds of woe,
        No maiden was by their side!"

JOHANN LUDWIG UHLAND
Translated by
Henry Wadsworth Longfellow

Der Gute Kamerad

Ich hatt' einen Kameraden,
Einen bessern findst du nit.
Die Trommel schlug zum Streite,
Er ging an meiner Seite
In gleichem Schritt und Tritt.

Eine Kugel kam geflogen;
Gilt's mir oder gilt es dir?
Ihn hat es weggerissen,
Er liegt mir vor den Füssen,
Als wär's ein Stück von mir.

Will mir die Hand noch reichen,
Derweil ich eben lad':
"Kann dir die Hand nicht geben,
Bleib du im ew'gen Leben.
Mein guter Kamerad!"

JOHANN LUDWIG UHLAND
1787–1862

110

The Good Comrade

I HAD a trusty comrade
No better man you'll see.
We heard the bugles blowing,
To war together going
Still side by side were we.

Then came a bullet flying;
For you, or me alone?
From me it tears him dying.
Now at my feet he's lying,
Oh, part of me is gone!

His hand is held toward me,
But I must load anew;
'Your hand I cannot hold, lad,
But bide you as of old, lad,
In heaven my comrade true!'

JOHANN LUDWIG UHLAND
Translated by Norman MacLeod

Wiegenlied

SINGET leise, leise, leise,
Singt ein flüsternd Wiegenlied,
Von dem Monde lernt die Weise,
Der so still am Himmel zieht.

Singt ein Lied so süss gelinde,
Wie die Quellen auf den Kieseln,
Wie die Bienen um die Linde
Summen, murmeln, flüstern, rieseln.

CLEMENS BRENTANO
1778–1842

Hymne

[*Aus* HYMNEN AN DIE NACHT]

DER Jüngling bist du, der seit langer Zeit
Auf unsren Gräbern steht in tiefem Sinnen;
Ein tröstlich Zeichen in der Dunkelheit—
Der höhern Menschneit freudiges Beginnen.
Was uns gesenkt in tiefe Traurigkeit,
Zieht uns mit süsser Sehnsucht nun von hinnen.
Im Tode ward das ew'ge Leben kund,
Du bist der Tod und machst uns erst gesund.

NOVALIS (Friedrich von Hardenberg)
1772–1801

Lullaby

SOFTLY, softly, softly croon,
Sing a whispered lullaby,
Learn the music from the moon
Moving still across the sky.

Sing a melody as tender
As the brook along the stones,
As the bees around the linden—
Humming, murmured, whispered tones.

CLEMENS BRENTANO
Translated by John W. Thomas

Hymn

[*From* HYMNS TO NIGHT]

YOU are that youth who long in meditation
Upon our graves has kept his face inclined;
A token in the dark, our consolation,
Joyful beginning of a new mankind.
The very power that wrought our sad prostration
Now moves our hearts to leave that gloom behind.
In death eternal life was first revealed,
That youth is death, by him our ills are healed.

NOVALIS (Friedrich von Hardenberg)
Translated by Michael Hamburger

Wenn nicht mehr Zahlen und Figuren

WENN nicht mehr Zahlen und Figuren
Sind Schlüssel aller Kreaturen,
Wenn die, so singen oder küssen,
Mehr als die Tiefgelehrten wissen,
Wenn sich die Welt ins freie Leben,
Und in die Welt wird zurückbegeben,
Wenn dann sich wieder Licht und Schatten
Zu echter Klarheit wieder gatten,
Und man in Märchen und Gedichten
Erkennt die wahren Weltgeschichten,
Dann fliegt vor einem geheimen Wort
Das ganze verkehrte Wesen fort.

NOVALIS (Friedrich von Hardenberg)
1772–1801

Wenn alle untreu werden...

WENN alle untreu werden,
So bleib' ich dir doch treu,
Dass Dankbarkeit auf Erden
Nicht ausgestorben sei.
Für mich umfing dich Leiden,
Vergingst für mich in Schmerz;
Drum geb' ich dir mit Freuden
Auf ewig dieses Herz.

When Geometric Diagrams . . .

WHEN geometric diagrams and digits
Are no longer the keys to living things,
When people who go about singing or kissing
Know deeper things than the great scholars,
When society is returned once more
To unimprisoned life, and to the universe,
And when light and darkness mate
Once more and make something entirely transparent,
And people see in poems and fairy tales
The true history of the world,
Then our entire twisted nature will turn
And run when a single secret word is spoken.

NOVALIS (Friedrich von Hardenberg)
Translated by Robert Bly

Though All Are Faithless Growing . . .

THOUGH all are faithless growing,
Yet will I faithful be,
That one on earth is showing
His thankfulness to Thee.
For me Thou cam'st to suffer
For me Thou had'st to smart,
And now with joy I offer
To Thee my thankful heart.

[Wenn alle untreu werden . . .]

Oft muss ich bitter weinen,
Dass du gestorben bist,
Und mancher von den Deinen
Dich lebenslang vergisst.
Von Liebe nur durchdrungen,
Hast du so viel getan,
Und doch bist du verklungen,
Und keiner denkt daran.

Du stehst voll treuer Liebe
Noch immer jedem bei,
Und wenn dir keiner bliebe,
So bleibst du dennoch treu;
Die treuste Liebe sieget,
Am Ende fühlt man sie,
Weint bitterlich und schmieget
Sich kindlich an dein Knie.

Ich habe dich empfunden,
O! lasse nicht von mir;
Lass innig mich verbunden
Auf ewig sein mit dir.
Einst schauen meine Brüder
Auch wieder himmelwärts
Und sinken liebend nieder
Und fallen dir ans Herz.

NOVALIS (Friedrich von Hardenberg)
1772–1801

[Though All Are Faithless Growing . . .]

> With tears I oft am grieving
> That Thou did'st need to die,
> While friends, Thy trust deceiving,
> Forgot and passed Thee by.
> With naught but love unsparing
> Thou cam'st for them and me.
> They let Thee die, uncaring,
> And thought no more of Thee.
>
> Thou standest still sustaining
> Each one with love anew;
> With not a friend remaining,
> Thou still art ever true.
> Yet true love ever winneth,
> At last the world will see,
> When weeping each one clingeth,
> A child before Thy knee.
>
> When now at last I find Thee,
> O leave me not alone!
> But ever closer bind me
> And let me be Thine own!
> My brothers too, beholding,
> Will soon in Heav'n find rest,
> And then Thy love enfolding
> Will sink upon Thy breast.

NOVALIS (Friedrich von Hardenberg)
Translated by Eileen Hutchins

Ehmals und Jetzt

In jüngern Tagen war ich des Morgens froh,
    Des Abends weint' ich; jetzt, da ich älter bin,
        Beginn ich zweifelnd meinen Tag, doch
            Heilig und heiter ist mir sein Ende.

FRIEDRICH HÖLDERLIN
1770–1843

Then and Now

IN younger days each morning I rose with joy,
   To weep at nightfall; now, in my later years,
    Though doubting I begin my day, yet
      Always its end is serene and holy.

FRIEDRICH HÖLDERLIN
Translated by Michael Hamburger

Hölderlin's Old Age

WHEN I was young I woke gladly in the morning
With the dew I grieved, towards the close of day.
Now, when I rise, I curse the white cascade
That refreshes all roots, and I wish my eyelids
Were shutters held down by the endless weight
Of the mineral earth. How strange it is,
    that at evening
When prolonged shadows lie down like cut hay
In my mad age, I rejoice, and my spirit sings
Burning intensely in the centre of a cold sky.

Adapted by STEPHEN SPENDER

Hyperions Schicksalslied

IHR wandelt droben im Licht
Auf weichem Boden, selige Genien!
Glänzende Götterlüfte
Rühren euch leicht,
Wie die Finger der Künstlerin
Heilige Saiten.

Schicksallos, wie der schlafende
Säugling, atmen die Himmlischen;
Keusch bewahrt
In bescheidener Knospe,
Blühet ewig
Ihnen der Geist,
Und die seligen Augen
Blicken in stiller
Ewiger Klarheit.

Doch uns ist gegeben,
Auf keiner Stätte zu ruhn,
Es schwinden, es fallen
Die leidenden Menschen
Blindlings von einer
Stunde zur andern,
Wie Wasser von Klippe
Zu Klippe geworfen,
Jahrlang ins Ungewisse hinab.

FRIEDRICH HÖLDERLIN
1770–1843

122

Hyperion's Song of Fate

You walk above in the light,
   Weightless tread a soft floor, blessed genii!
      Radiant the gods' mild breezes
        Gently play on you
          As the girl artist's fingers
          On holy strings.

Fateless the Heavenly breathe
   Like an unweaned infant asleep;
      Chastely preserved
        In modest bud
          For ever their minds
          Are in flower
            And their blissful eyes
              Eternally tranquil gaze.
              Eternally clear.

But we are fated
   To find no foothold, no rest,
      And suffering mortals
        Dwindle and fall
          Headlong from one
          Hour to the next,
            Hurled like water
              From ledge to ledge
                Downward for years to the vague abyss.

FRIEDRICH HÖLDERLIN
Translated by Michael Hamburger

Die Heimat

Froh kehrt der Schiffer heim an den stillen Strom,
Von Inseln fernher, wenn er geerntet hat;
    So käm' auch ich zur Heimat, hätt' ich
      Güter so viele, wie Leid, geerntet.

Ihr teuern Ufer, die mich erzogen einst,
Stillt ihr der Liebe Leiden, versprecht ihr mir,
    Ihr Wälder meiner Jugend, wenn ich
      Komme, die Ruhe noch einmal wieder?

Am kühlen Bache, wo ich der Wellen Spiel,
Am Strome, wo ich gleiten die Schiffe sah,
    Dort bin ich bald; euch, traute Berge,
      Die mich behüteten einst, der Heimat

Verehrte sichre Grenzen, der Mutter Haus
Und liebender Geschwister Umarmungen
    Begrüss' ich bald und ihr umschliesst mich,
      Dass, wie in Banden, das Herz mir heile,

Ihr treu geblieb'nen! aber ich weiss, ich weiss,
Der Liebe Leid, dies heilet so bald mir nicht,
    Dies singt kein Wiegengesang, den tröstend
      Sterbliche singen, mir aus dem Busen.

Home

GLAD steers the sailor home to the quiet stream
From far-off islands, when he has harvested.
    So would I, too, come home, if I had
   Harvested riches to vie with sorrow.

You faithful shores, forsaken, that nursed me once,
Will you still the sorrows of love, will you promise me,
    You forests of my youth, if I
   Come, the peace of the heart once more?

At the cool brook where I watched the play of waves,
The river where I gazed at the gliding ships,
    There, soon, I'll be; you dearest mountains,
   You that protected me once, the home's

Honored, inviolate boundaries, my mother's house,
And loving embraces, brothers' and sister's arms,
    I feel them soon, and you surround me
   That, as in bonds, my heart be healed.

You true, you steadfast ones! But I know, I know,
The wound of love, this cannot so quickly heal;
    This no cradlesong mortals pitying
   Sing to the comfortless, drives from my breast.

[*Die Heimat*]

Denn sie, die uns das himmlische Feuer leihn,
Die Götter schenken heiliges Leid uns auch.
Drum bleibe dies. Ein Sohn der Erde
Schein' ich; zu lieben gemacht, zu leiden.

FRIEDRICH HÖLDERLIN
1770–1843

An die Parzen

Nur einen Sommer gönnt, ihr Gewaltigen!
Und einen Herbst zu reifem Gesange mir,
Dass williger mein Herz, vom süssen
Spiele gesättiget, dann mir sterbe!

Die Seele, der im Leben ihr göttlich Recht
Nicht ward, sie ruht auch drunten in Orkus nicht;
Doch ist mir einst das Heil'ge, das am
Herzen mir liegt, das Gedicht, gelungen,

Willkommen dann, o Stille der Schattenwelt!
Zufrieden bin ich, wenn auch mein Saitenspiel
Mich nicht hinabgeleitet; Einmal
Lebt' ich, wie Götter, und mehr bedarf's nicht.

FRIEDRICH HÖLDERLIN
1770–1843

[*Home*]

For they, the gods, who lend us the heavenly fire,
This holy sorrow also impart to us.
    So let it be. A son of Earth
   Am I: to love I was formed, to grieve.

FRIEDRICH HÖLDERLIN
Translated by Vernon Watkins

To the Fates

ONE summer only grant me, you powerful Fates,
   And one more autumn only for mellow song,
     So that more willingly, replete with
       Music's late sweetness, my heart may die then.

The soul in life denied its god-given right
   Down there in Oreus also will find no peace;
     But when what's holy, dear to me, the
       Poem's accomplished, my art perfected,

Then welcome, silence, welcome cold world of shades!
   I'll be content, though here I must leave my lyre
     And singless travel down; for once I
       Lived like the gods, and no more is needed.

FRIEDRICH HÖLDERLIN
Translated by Michael Hamburger

Columbus

STEURE, mutiger Segler! Es mag der Witz dich verhöhnen,
Und der Schiffer am Steu'r senken die lässige Hand.
Immer, immer nach West! Dort muss die Küste sich zeigen,
    Liegt sie doch deutlich und liegt schimmernd vor deinem
      Verstand.
Traue dem leitenden Gott und folge dem schweigenden
      Weltmeer!
Wär' sie noch nicht, sie stieg' jetzt aus den Fluten empor.
Mit dem Genius steht die Natur im ewigen Bunde;
Was der eine verspricht, leistet die andre gewiss.

FRIEDRICH VON SCHILLER
1759–1805

Poesie

MICH hält kein Band, mich fesselt keine Schranke,
Frei schwing' ich mich durch alle Räume fort,
Mein unermesslich Reich ist der Gedanke,
Und mein geflügelt Werkzeug ist das Wort.
Was sich bewegt im Himmel und auf Erden,
Was die Natur tief im Verborgnen schafft,
Muss mir entschleiert und entsiegelt werden,
Denn nichts beschränkt die freie Dichterkraft;
Doch Schönres find' ich nichts, wie lang ich wähle,
Als in der schönen Form—die schöne Seele.

FRIEDRICH VON SCHILLER
1759–1805

Columbus

S AIL on, oh captain! Though the mockers grin
And though the helm slip from a heedless hand,
Forever westward! There is a land
Which shall receive you. You have seen
Its shore before your eyes. Trust your skills.
Though oceans may be empty on their verge—
You willed a land. It shall rise from the surge.
For nature always yields what human spirit wills.

FRIEDRICH VON SCHILLER
Translated by Vladimir Rus

Poesie

N o bonds can hold, no bounds can hem my flight,
I soar through space as freely as a bird;
my endless realm is thought, my throne is light,
my winged sceptre is the living word.
All things which move in heaven and on earth
must lift their veils and break their seals for me,
and all which nature secretly gives birth
is subject to the power of poetry.
Yet nothing can I find more fair and warm
than the lovely soul within the lovely form.

FRIEDRICH VON SCHILLER
Adapted by John W. Thomas

Aus "An die Freude"

I

FREUDE, schöner Götterfunken,
Tochter aus Elysium
Wir betreten feuertrunken,
Himmlische, dein Heiligtum.
Deine Zauber binden wieder,
Was die Mode streng geteilt,
Alle Menschen werden Brüder,
Wo dein sanfter Flügel weilt.
    Seid umschlungen, Millionen!
    Diesen Kuss der ganzen Welt!
    Brüder—überm Sternenzelt
    Muss ein lieber Vater wohnen.

V

Aus der Wahrheit Feuerspiegel
Lächelt sie den Forscher an
Zu der Tugend steilem Hügel
Leitet sie des Dulders Bahn.
Auf des Glaubens Sonnenberge
Sieht man ihre Fahnen wehn,
Durch den Riss gesprengter Särge
Sie im Chor der Engel stehn.
    Duldet mutig, Millionen!
    Duldet für die bessre Welt!
    Droben überm Sternenzelt
    Wird ein grosser Gott belohnen.

FRIEDRICH VON SCHILLER
1759–1805

From "Ode to Joy"

I

Joy, of flame celestial fashioned,
  Daughter of Elysium,
By that holy fire impassioned
  To thy sanctuary we come.
Thine the spells that reunited
  Those estranged by Custom dread,
Every man a brother plighted
  Where thy gentle wings are spread.
  Millions in our arms we gather,
  To the world our kiss be sent!
  Past the starry firmament,
Brothers, dwells a loving Father.

V

She from Truth's own mirror shining
  Casts on sages glances gay,
Guides the sufferer unrepining
  Far up Virtue's steepest way;
On the hills of Faith all-glorious
  Mark her sunlit banners fly,
She, in death's despite, victorious,
  Stands with angels in the sky.
    Millions, bravely sorrows bearing,
      Suffer for a better time!
      See, above the starry clime
God a great reward preparing.

FRIEDRICH VON SCHILLER
Translated by Norman MacLeod

Freudvoll und Leidvoll

[*Aus* EGMONT]

FREUDVOLL
Und leidvoll,
Gedankenvoll sein;
Langen
Und bangen
In schwebender Pein;
Himmelhoch jauchzend,
Zum Tode betrübt;
Glücklich allein
Ist die Seele, die liebt.

JOHANN WOLFGANG VON GOETHE
1749–1832

Klärchen's Song

[*From* EGMONT]

JOYFUL
And sorrowful,
Pondering, intense;
Hanging
And trembling
In floating suspense;
Death-sad, exulting
To heaven above;
Happy is none
But the soul that can love.

JOHANN WOLFGANG VON GOETHE
Translated by Vera Lachmann

Lied des Türmers

[*Aus* FAUST]

ZUM Sehen geboren
Zum Schauen bestellt,
Dem Turme geschworen,
Gefällt mir die Welt.
Ich blick in die Ferne,
Ich seh in der Näh,
Den Mond und die Sterne,
Den Wald und das Reh.
So seh ich in allen
Die ewige Zier,
Und wie mir's gefallen,
Gefall ich auch mir.
Ihr glücklichen Augen,
Was je ihr gesehn,
Es sei, wie es wolle,
Er war doch so schön!

JOHANN WOLFGANG VON GOETHE
1749–1832

134

Deep Night

[*From* FAUST]

FOR seeing begotten,
My sight my employ,
And sworn to the watch-tower,
The world gives me joy.
I gaze in the distance,
I mark in the near
The moon and the planets,
The woods and the deer.
So find I in all things
Eternal delight,
The more that they please me
Am pleased to have sight.
Oh eyes, what has reached you,
So gladly aware,
Whatever its outcome,
At least it was fair.

JOHANN WOLFGANG VON GOETHE
Translated by Louis MacNeice

Prolog im Himmel

[*Aus* FAUST]

RAPHAEL: Die Sonne tönt nach alter Weise
In Brudersphären Wettgesang,
Und ihre vorgeschriebne Reise
Vollendet sie mit Donnergang.
Ihr Anblick gibt den Engeln Stärke,
Wenn keiner sie ergründen mag;
Die unbegreiflich hohen Werke
Sind herrlich wie am ersten Tag.

GABRIEL: Und schnell und unbegreiflich schnelle
Dreht sich umher der Erde Pracht;
Es wechselt Paradieseshelle
Mit tiefer, schauervoller Nacht;
Es schäumt das Meer in breiten Flüssen
Am tiefen Grund der Felsen auf,
Und Fels und Meer wird fortgerissen
In ewig schnellem Sphärenlauf.

MICHAEL: Und Stürme brausen um die Wette,
Vom Meer aufs Land, vom Land aufs Meer,
Und bilden wütend eine Kette
Der tiefsten Wirkung rings umher.
Da flammt ein blitzendes Verheeren
Dem Pfade vor des Donnerschlags;
Doch deine Boten, Herr, verehren
Das sanfte Wandeln deines Tags.

Prologue in Heaven

[From FAUST*]*

RAPHAEL: The chanting sun, as ever, rivals
The chanting of his brother spheres
And marches round his destined circuit—
A march that thunders in our ears.
His aspect cheers the Hosts of Heaven
Though what his essence none can say;
These inconceivable creations
Keep the high state of their first day.

GABRIEL: And swift, with inconceivable swiftness,
The earth's full splendour rolls around,
Celestial radiance alternating
With a dread night too deep to sound;
The sea against the rocks' deep bases
Comes foaming up in far-flung force,
And rock and sea go whirling onward
In the swift spheres' eternal course.

MICHAEL: And storms in rivalry are raging
From sea to land, from land to sea,
In frenzy forge the world a girdle
From which no inmost part is free.
The blight of lightning flaming yonder
Marks where the thunder-bolt will play;
And yet Thine envoys, Lord, revere
The gentle movement of Thy day.

[*Prolog im Himmel*]

ZU DREI: Der Anblick gibt den Engeln Stärke,
Da keiner dich ergründen mag,
Und alle deine hohen Werke
Sind herrlich wie am ersten Tag.

JOHANN WOLFGANG VON GOETHE
1749–1832

Wanderers Nachtlied

ÜBER allen Gipfeln
Ist Ruh,
In allen Wipfeln
Spürest du
Kaum einen Hauch;
Die Vögelein schweigen im Walde.
Warte nur, balde
Ruhest du auch.

JOHANN WOLFGANG VON GOETHE
1749–1832

[Prologue in Heaven]

CHOIR OF ANGELS:

> Thine aspect cheers the Hosts of Heaven
> Though what Thine essence none can say,
> And all Thy loftiest creations
> Keep the high state of their first day.

JOHANN WOLFGANG VON GOETHE
Translated by Louis MacNeice

Wanderer's Night Song

> O'ER all the hill-tops
> Is quiet now,
> In all the tree-tops
> Hearest thou
> Hardly a breath;
> The birds are asleep in the trees:
> Wait; soon like these
> Thou too shalt rest.

JOHANN WOLFGANG VON GOETHE
Translated by
Henry Wadsworth Longfellow

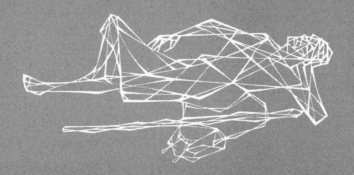

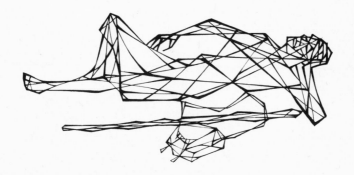

Mignons Lied

[*Aus* WILHELM MEISTER]

KENNST du das Land, wo die Zitronen blühn,
Im dunkeln Laub die Gold-Orangen glühn,
Ein sanfter Wind vom blauen Himmel weht,
Die Myrte still und hoch der Lorbeer steht?
Kennst du es wohl?—Dahin! Dahin
Möcht' ich mit dir, o mein Geliebter, ziehn.

Kennst du das Haus? Auf Säulen ruht sein Dach,
Es glänzt der Saal, es schimmert das Gemach,
Und Marmorbilder stehn und sehn mich an:
Was hat man dir, du armes Kind, getan?
Kennst du es wohl?—Dahin! Dahin
Möcht' ich mit dir, o mein Beschützer, ziehn.

Kennst du den Berg und seinen Wolkensteg?
Das Maultier sucht im Nebel seinen Weg;
In Höhlen wohnt der Drachen alte Brut;
Es stürzt der Fels und über ihn die Flut.
Kennst du ihn wohl?—Dahin! Dahin
Geht unser Weg! o Vater, lass uns ziehn!

JOHANN WOLFGANG VON GOETHE
1749–1832

Mignon's Song

[*From* WILHELM MEISTER]

KNOWEST thou the land where bloom the lemon trees,
And darkly gleam the golden oranges?
A gentle wind blows down from that blue sky;
Calm stands the myrtle and the laurel high.
Knowest thou the land? So far and fair!
Thou, whom I love, and I will wander there.

Knowest thou the house with all its rooms aglow,
And shining hall and columned portico?
The marble statues stand and look at me.
Alas, poor child, what have they done to thee?
Knowest thou the land? So far and fair.
My Guardian, thou and I will wander there.

Knowest thou the mountain with its bridge of cloud?
The mule plods warily: the white mists crowd.
Coiled in their caves the brood of dragons sleep;
The torrent hurls the rock from steep to steep.
Knowest thou the land? So far and fair.
Father, away! Our road is over there!

JOHANN WOLFGANG VON GOETHE
Translated by James Elroy Flecker

Die Namen

Ich fragte meine Schöne:
Wie soll mein Lied dich nennen?
Soll dich als Dorimene,
Als Galathee, als Chloris,
Als Lesbia, als Doris,
Die Welt der Enkel kennen?

Ach! Namen sind nur Töne:
Sprach meine holde Schöne.
Wähl' selbst. Du kannst mich Doris,
Und Galathee und Chloris
Und—wie du willst, mich nennen;
Nur nenne mich die Deine.

GOTTHOLD EPHRAIM LESSING
1729–1781

Names

I ASKED my fair one happy day,
What I should call her in my lay;
  By what sweet name from Rome or Greece;
Lalage, Neaera, Chloris
Sappho, Lesbia, or Doris
  Arethusa or Lucrece.

'Ah!' replied my gentle fair,
'Beloved, what are names but air?
  Choose thou whatever suits the line;
Call me Sappho, call me Chloris,
Call me Lalage or Doris,
  Only, only call me Thine.'

GOTTHOLD EPHRAIM LESSING
Translated by Samuel Taylor Coleridge

An einen Boten

WENN du zu mei'm Schätzel kommst,
Sag: ich liess sie grüssen;
Wenn sie fraget, wie mir's geht,
Sag: auf beiden Füssen.

Wenn sie fraget, ob ich krank,
Sag: ich sei gestorben;
Wenn sie an zu weinen fangt,
Sag: ich käme morgen.

ANONYMOUS

Westphalian Song

WHEN thou to my true-love com'st
   Greet her from me kindly;
When she asks thee how I fare?
   Say, folks in Heaven fare finely.

When she asks, "What! Is he sick?"
   Say, dead!—and when for sorrow
She begins to sob and cry,
   Say, I come tomorrow.

ANONYMOUS
Translated by
Samuel Taylor Coleridge

Ännchen von Tharau

ÄNNCHEN von Tharau ist, die mir gefällt;
Sie ist mein Leben, mein Gut und mein Geld.
Ännchen von Tharau wieder hat ihr Herz
Auf mich gerichtet in Lieb' und in Schmerz.
Ännchen von Tharau, mein Reichtum, mein Gut,
Du meine Seele, mein Fleisch und mein Blut!

Käm' alles Wetter gleich auf uns zu schlahn,
Wir sind gesinnt bei einander zu stahn!
Krankheit, Verfolgung, Betrübnis und Pein
Soll uns' rer Liebe Verknotigung sein.
Ännchen von Tharau, mein Licht und mein' Sonn',
Mein Leben schliess' ich um deines herum.

Attributed to SIMON DACH
1605–1659

Annie of Tharaw

ANNIE of Tharaw, my true love of old,
She is my life, and my good, and my gold.
Annie of Tharaw, her heart once again
To me has surrendered in joy and in pain.
Annie of Tharaw, my riches, my good,
Thou, O my soul, my flesh, and my blood!

Then come the wild weather, come sleet
    or come snow,
We will stand by each other, however it blow.
Oppression, and sickness, and sorrow, and pain,
Shall be to our true love as links to the chain.
Annie of Tharaw, my light and my sun,
The threads of our two lives are woven in one.

Attributed to SIMON DACH
Translated by
Henry Wadsworth Longfellow

Ein' feste Burg ist unser Gott

EIN feste Burg ist unser Gott,
Ein gute Wehr und Waffen;
Er hilft uns frei aus aller Not,
Die uns itzt hat betroffen.
Der alt böse Feind
Mit Ernst er's itzt meint;
Gross Macht und viel List
Sein grausam Rüstung ist,
Auf Erd ist nicht seins gleichen.

Mit unsrer Macht ist nichts getan,
Wir sind gar bald verloren;
Es streit für uns der rechte Mann,
Den Gott hat selbst erkoren.
Fragst du, wer der ist?
Er heisst Jesus Christ,
Der Herr Zebaoth,
Und ist kein andrer Gott,
Das Feld muss er behalten.

Und wenn die Welt voll Teufel wär'
Und wollt' uns gar verschlingen,
So fürchten wir uns nicht so sehr,
Es soll uns doch gelingen.
Der Fürst dieser Welt,
Wie sauer er sich stellt,
Tut er uns doch nicht;
Das macht, er ist gericht:
Ein Wörtlein kann ihn fällen.

A Mighty Fortress Is Our God

A MIGHTY fortress is our God,
A bulwark never failing,
Our helper He, amid the flood
Of mortal ill prevailing;
For still our ancient foe
Doth seek to work us woe,
His craft and power are great,
And armed with cruel hate,
On earth is not his equal.

Did we in our strength confide,
Our striving would be losing,
Were not the right man on our side,
The man of God's own choosing.
Dost ask who that may be?
Christ Jesus, it is he,
Lord Sabaoth his name,
From age to age the same,
And he must win the battle.

And though this world, with devils filled,
Should threaten to undo us,
We will not fear, for God hath willed
His truth to triumph through us.
The Prince of Darkness grim,
We tremble not at him,
His rage we can endure,
For lo! his doom is sure,
Our little word shall fell him.

Das Wort sie sollen lassen stahn
Und kein Dank dazu haben;
Er ist bei uns wohl auf dem Plan
Mit seinem Geist und Gaben.
Nehmen sie den Leib,
Gut, Ehr, Kind und Weib;
Lass fahren dahin!
Sie haben's kein Gewinn;
Das Reich muss uns doch bleiben.

MARTIN LUTHER
1483–1546

[*A Mighty Fortress Is Our God*]

That word above all earthly powers—
No thanks for them,—abideth;
The spirit and the gift is ours,
Through him who with us sideth.
Let goods and kindred go,
This mortal life also;
The body they may kill,
God's truth abideth still,
His kingdom is forever.

MARTIN LUTHER
Translated by F. H. Hedge

Winterrose

Es ist ein' Ros' entsprungen
Aus einer Wurzel zart,
Als uns die Alten sungen;
Aus Jesse kam die Art
Und hat ein Blümlein bracht
Mitten im kalten Winter
Wohl zu der halben Nacht.

Das Röslein, das ich meine,
Davon Esaias sagt,
Hat uns gebracht alleine
Marie die reine Magd:
Aus Gottes ew'gem Rat'
Hat sie ein Kind geboren,
Wohl zu der halben Nacht.

ANONYMOUS
16th Century

A Lovely Rose Is Sprung

A LOVELY rose is sprung,
Out of a tender root,
As men of old have sung,
From Jesse's stem a shoot.
And so a flower bright
Has bloomed in coldest winter
E'en in the deepest night.

The little rose I mean
Whereof Isaiah told,
Pure Mary, maid serene
Brought forth alone—behold:
Through God's eternal might
A little child she bore us
E'en in the deepest night.

ANONYMOUS
Translated by Margarete Münsterberg

155

Halmorakel

In einem zwîvellîchen wân
Was ich gesezzen und gedâhte,
Ich wolte von ir dienste gân,
Wan daz ein trôst mich wider brâhte.
Trôst mag ez rehte niht geheizen, owê des!
Ez ist vil kûme ein kleinez trœstelin:
Sô kleine, swenne ichz iu gesage, ir spottet mîn,
Doch frœut sich lützel ieman, er enwizze wes.

Mich hat ein halm gemachet frô:
Er giht, ich sül genâde vinden.
Ich maz daz selbe kleine strô,
als ich hie vor gesach von kinden.
Nû hœret unde merket ob siz denne tuo:
"Si tuot, si entuot, si tuot, si entuot, si tuot."
Swie dicke ich alsô maz, sô was daz ende ie guot,
Daz trœstet mich: dâ hœret ouch geloube zuo.

WALTHER VON DER VOGELWEIDE
About 1168–1230

Straw Prophecy

Hope of my lady's love lay dying.
I thought then, as I sat upon the ground,
I'd leave off my sighing.
Then consolation brought me round.
Consolation? Hardly that, ah woe.
Cold comfort is the best thing I can see,
If I should tell you, you'd make sport of me.
But—the reason suits me,—that I know.

A blade of straw brings joy today
It says that luck will come my way.
I measure it as children do
To find out if she loves me true.
O look and listen here.
She loves, she loves me not. I am her dear.
However oft I played this game
The answer "yes" came just the same.
So I am gay. Yet, belief belongs here too.

WALTHER VON DER VOGELWEIDE

159

Frühlingstrost

Ahî nu kumet uns diu zît,
Der kleinen vogellîne sanc.
Ez gruonet wol diu linde breit,
Zergangen ist der winter lanc.
Nu siht man bluomen wol getân:
an der héide üebent sie ir schîn.
Des wirt manic herze frô:
des selben trœstet sich daz mîn.

DIETMAR VON EIST
12th Century

Heart's Ease

HEY nonny-no, this is the time
When the little birds do sing.
Wide stretch the green limbs of the lime.
Winter is gone—it is the spring.
Now we see the flowers bloom.
On the green heath their splendors shine.
Many a heart makes room for joy
And solace enters into mine.

DIETMAR VON EIST
12th Century

Biographies of the Poets

INGEBORG BACHMANN (1926-), who was born in Klagenfurt, Austria, and studied philosophy in Vienna, lived for a time in Italy and Switzerland before settling in Berlin. In addition to poetry, she has written stories, radio plays, and an opera libretto. She has been given several German literary prizes for her work, including the Büchner award in 1964.

GOTTFRIED BENN (1886-1956) was born in Mansfield, Prussia. He studied medicine in Berlin. His experiences as a medical orderly before and during the First World War form the subject of most of his early work. In both his poetry and his short stories he was strongly influenced by Nietzsche. The collection of expressionist verse entitled *Morgue* is one of his best-known works.

BERTOLT BRECHT (1898-1956), one of the most powerful and influential figures in the contemporary theater, was born in Augsburg. He began his career by writing biting expressionist drama, proclaiming no particular political doctrine but savagely indicting twentieth-century society. In all his later works he strongly supported Marxism. After 1933 Brecht lived for fifteen years as an exile in Denmark, Finland, and the United States. In 1948 he returned to East Germany where he founded his own theater company, the famous Berliner Ensemble. Many of his plays are well known, perhaps especially *Die Dreigroschenoper* (*The Threepenny Opera*), which he wrote in collaboration with Kurt Weill.

CLEMENS BRENTANO (1778-1842) was born in Ehrenbreitsten, where his family was active in literary circles. One of the leaders of the German romantic movement, he studied in Germany and Vienna, before spending several years in a Catholic monastery. Fantastic imagery and a genius for capturing the German folk spirit are among the outstanding qualities of his work.

PAUL CELAN (1920-) was born in Czernowitz, in what was then Northern Romania, and began the study of medicine. When his town was occupied by the Russians, he fled to Vienna and studied literature there. In 1948 he moved to Paris, where he became a professor of literature. His poems speak of love and sorrow, which he depicts with surrealistic images. Critics have stated that much of his poetry is reminiscent of the paintings of Paul Klee.

163

SIMON DACH (1605-1659), born in Memel, East Prussia, became professor of poetry at the University of Königsberg in 1639. He wrote many excellent hymns, and was a leader in the early baroque movement.

DIETMAR VON EIST (12th century), born in Austria, was a member of the lesser nobility. Two of his relatives were also known as poets. His work belongs to the older group of minnesongs. Preceding in time the influence of the Provençal troubadours, his lines follow a traditional formal pattern of rhyme.

ANNETTE VON DROSTE-HÜLSHOFF (1797-1848) was born in Hülshoff and educated at home by private tutors. Her parents were members of the Catholic nobility. Ballads that combine vivid renderings of natural scenes from her homeland with a graceful narrative are among her most notable works. Her famous novella *Die Judenbuche (The Jew's Beech Tree)* evokes a powerful sense of the mysterious workings of fate and of the author's deeply religious nature.

JOSEPH VON EICHENDORFF (1788-1857) was born in Silesia. He studied law and spent some time as a volunteer in the Prussian army. One of the greatest lyric poets of the romantic movement, he also translated religious dramas and wrote tragedies. Many of his poems were set to music by Schubert and Schumann.

ERICH FRIED (1920-   ), who was born in Vienna, emigrated to London in 1938. Before devoting all his time to writing, he worked as a chemist and in a glass factory. A love of children's fairy tales, magic, and myth is reflected in his poems. He also reveals a passionate involvement with the problems of the contemporary world. Fried has translated the work of T. S. Eliot, Dylan Thomas, and many other major poets into German.

STEFAN GEORGE (1868-1933) attended school in Darmstadt, before studying and traveling all over the European continent and England. His poetry is filled with esoteric mythical allusions and rich imagery. *Der Stern des Bundes (The Star of the League)* and *Das neue Reich (The New Kingdom)* are two of his most famous collections. He also translated many important literary works from French, English, and Italian.

JOHANN WOLFGANG VON GOETHE (1779-1832) is known as one of the greatest men in European literature. He was born in Frankfurt am Main, and although he later traveled extensively, his life and work always centered about the court at Weimar. There, in addition to his literary activities, he held an important cabinet post, directed a theater, and carried on extensive scientific research. A many-faceted genius, Goethe exerted an enormous influence on the culture and thought of his period. *Faust* is perhaps his most famous work, but he also wrote much beautiful lyric poetry, a number of novels and volumes of criticism, and many other dramas.

GÜNTER GRASS (1927-   ), who was born in Danzig, now lives in Berlin. Known chiefly as a novelist, he also has a reputation as a sculptor, painter, playwright, and poet. His novels, published in this country under the titles of *The Tin Drum, The Dog Years,* and *Cat and Mouse,* have been translated into English and every major European language.

HEINRICH HEINE (1797-1856) was born in Düsseldorf and began a business career with the help of his uncle. It was a failure, adding to his difficulties with the authorities because of his Jewish descent. Trips to England and Italy preceded his decision to live permanently in Paris, where he went in 1830. Heine wrote in French as well as in German, and aimed much of his journalistic and critical activities at promoting understanding between the two countries. His writings reflect his lifelong passionate concern with justice and liberty.

HERMANN HESSE (1877-1962), novelist and poet, was born in the Swabian city of Calw. His early career was greatly influenced by Novalis and the other German romanticists. He developed a highly individual style of his own, however, characterized by psychoanalytic and Eastern spiritual insights. Hesse became a Swiss citizen in 1921, and was awarded the Nobel Prize for literature in 1946. *Der Steppenwolf* and *Siddartha* are two of his best-known novels.

HUGO VON HOFMANNSTHAL (1874-1929) was born and educated in Vienna. He is known as both poet and dramatist, but his remarkable gifts may perhaps best be seen in the texts he provided for many of the operas of Richard Strauss. His early poetry was written when impressionism was popular, and, like the poetry of his friend Stefan George, combines mysticism and exoticism with a delicate balance in form. After the First World War he believed that the cultural heritage of Europe was imperiled, and with Max Reinhardt he helped to found the Salzburg Festival.

FRIEDRICH HÖLDERLIN (1770-1843), born at Lauffen on the Neckar River, was greatly influenced by Schiller, who befriended him. Destined for the ministry, he studied theology and at various times earned his living as a tutor. An unhappy platonic love affair preceded his first lapse into ınsanity. Throughout the rest of his life, he alternated between periods of madness and sanity. His lyric poetry and his novel *Hyperion* are considered among the masterpieces of the German language.

VERA LACHMANN (1904-   ) studied in Berlin, where she was born, and in Switzerland. In 1939 she emigrated to the United States, and became professor of classics at Brooklyn College.

ELSE LASKER-SCHÜLER (1869-1945), born in Elberfeld, was inspired by the beauty of the Rhineland as well as by her deep commitment to Judaism. After her first marriage to a physician ended in divorce, she married Herwath Walden, editor of *Der Strum.* Considered a leader among her contemporaries, she expressed great artistry and imagination in her poems. She emigrated from Nazi Germany and died in Palestine.

NIKOLAUS LENAU, pseudonym of Nikolaus von Strehlenau (1802-1850), was born in Hungary and studied in Vienna. He came to the United States in 1832, and lived in Maryland and Ohio for a year before his return to Vienna. His poetry is filled with vivid images and morbid thoughts. Periods of depression marked his life, and he died in an insane asylum.

GOTTHOLD EPHRAIM LESSING (1729-1781), the noted dramatist and critic, was born in Kamenz, Saxony. He studied theology and Greek literature, but an early fascination with the theater led him to fame as a playwright. He was also responsible for translations from the French, contemporary criticism, and many theological works. The essay *Laokoon* (*Laocoön*) and the play *Minna von Barnhelm* are two of his most famous works.

MARTIN LUTHER (1483-1546), the great religious reformer, was born in Eisleben in the Harz Mountains. He was professor of Biblical exegis at Wittenberg when in 1517 he nailed to the church door his 95 theses, attacking the Roman Catholic Church for its sale of indulgences. In addition to his polemical prose writings and his translations of the Old and the New Testament, Luther wrote many hymns.

CHRISTIAN MORGENSTERN (1874-1914), born in Munich, was the son and grandson of well-known painters. He is most famous for the grotesque humor of his *Galgenlieder* (*Gallows Songs*), but he also wrote very beautiful, serious lyric poetry.

EDUARD MÖRIKE (1804-1875) is known as the most gifted of all the poets belonging to the so-called Swabian school. Born in Ludwigsburg, he studied theology and served for many years as a country pastor. Though outwardly his life seemed quiet, he suffered from melancholy and religious doubts. He sometimes wrote folklike lyrics, but in his more characteristic vein, he was capable of a powerful classical style, not unlike that of Hölderlin.

FRIEDRICH NIETZSCHE (1844-1900), the famed philosopher, was born in Rocken, Saxony. The descendant of three generations of Lutheran pastors, he was educated at Bonn and at Leipzig. He became professor of classical philology at Basel and subsequently lived in Italy until his mental breakdown in 1889 from which he never recovered. Although his works have often been misunderstood, he exerted an enormous influence on twentieth-century thought, particularly on the development of expressionist poetry and on the writings of such men as Thomas Mann and Jean-Paul Sartre.

NOVALIS is the pen name of Friedrich von Hardenberg (1772-1801), generally recognized as the leading poet of the early romantic movement in Germany. He was born in Saxony, and studied law and philosophy. His belief that man had once lived in complete unity with the natural world developed into a unique personal faith. After the death of his fiancée, in such works as the prose poems *Hymnen an die Nacht* (*Hymns to the Night*), he expressed a mystical yearning for death. The symbol of the blue flower, the symbol that represents all of German romanticism, was taken from Novalis' novel *Heinrich von Ofterdingen*.

RAINER MARIA RILKE (1875-1926) was born in Prague of old Bohemian stock. After attending military academy he studied at various universities. His early poems are highly subjective expressions of half-religious, half-aesthetic ecstasy. The sculptor Auguste Rodin was a close friend and influenced Rilke in the poems, which are meticulously descriptive of objects, animals, and people. Besides his poetry, Rilke is known for his sensitive works of prose, his extensive letters, and his journals. Considered the most significant figure in twentieth-century German lyric poetry, he had already attained an international reputation before his death.

FRIEDRICH RÜCKERT (1788-1866) was born in Schweinfurt and studied classical Eastern languages and literature, particularly Persian and Arabic. He is known especially for his pioneering efforts in popularizing Oriental poetic forms and philosophical ideas in Germany. His collection *Kindertotenlieder* (*Songs on Children's Deaths*) was set to music by Mahler, and he also published many translations from Oriental literature.

NELLY SACHS (1891-   ) was born in Berlin and fled with her mother to Stockholm in 1940. All the other members of Miss Sachs's family disappeared in Nazi Germany. Her poetry is profoundly influenced by ancient Jewish and Biblical themes. With Schmuel Yosel Agnon, Miss Sachs was awarded the Nobel Prize for literature in 1966. She now lives in Stockholm, and has published several anthologies of her poetry and translations of Swedish poetry into German.

FRIEDRICH VON SCHILLER (1759-1805), one of the important figures in German literature, was born in Marbach. His early tragedies were bitter social comments, and he was arrested for publishing them. He fled to Mannheim and earned his living as a historian. His masterpieces of reflective poetry came after 1794, when he began a close association with Goethe. Greek, French, and English drama were strong influences on his later works. *Wilhelm Tell* and *Don Carlos* are two of his most famous plays.

GEORG TRAKL (1887-1914) was born in Salzburg, Austria, and educated in Vienna. He served as a medical orderly in the opening weeks of the First World War. But his life was disrupted by fits of depression and despair, and he died from an overdose of cocaine. Melancholy images and a deep anguish are reflected in his poems.

JOHANN LUDWIG UHLAND (1787-1862), born in Tübingen, studied law and literature. Besides an active career in the government and as a lawyer, he was an expert in German mythology and folklore. His historical ballads include *Roland* and *Taillifer*. Many of his ballads have been set to music by Schubert and other composers.

WALTHER VON DER VOGELWEIDE (c. 1168-1230) is generally known as the greatest lyric poet of medieval Germany. He was probably born in the South Tyrol and began his career as poet and minstrel at the court of Vienna around 1190. His early poems and songs are highly stylized forms of the period, but he later broke away from tradition and composed more original lyric works, using nature as his background.

FRANZ WERFEL (1890-1945), Austrian poet, novelist, and playwright, was born in Prague. He was an editor for a German publishing company at the outbreak of the First World War. After serving in the army, he went to Vienna in 1918 and married the widow of Gustav Mahler. Fleeing from the Nazis, he went to Paris in 1938 and came to the United States in 1940, where he died in California. Although he is best known for his novels, many critics believe Werfel to be the foremost lyric poet of the German expressionist movement.

168

Index of Titles

Index of Titles

Index of Titles

Index of Titles

Index of First Lines

174

Index of First Lines

Index of Poets

Index of Poets

Index of Translators

Index of Translators

Mason, Eudo C., 65
Mead, Ruth and Matthew, 29
Middleton, Christopher, 35
Morwitz, Ernst, 79, 81
Münsterberg, Margarete, 155

Rothenberg, Jerome, 17
Rus, Vladimir, 129

Snow, Edith Abercrombie, 33, 37
Spender, Stephen, 67, 121
Stork, Stephen, 83

Thomas, John W., 99, 101, 105, 113, 129

Valhope, Carol North, 79, 81

Watkins, Vernon, 69, 85, 125

Zohn, Harry, 19

ABOUT THE COMPILER

Helen Plotz is deeply involved in awakening young people to an appreciation of poetry. Her previous volumes—*Imagination's Other Place: Poems of Science and Mathematics, Untune the Sky: Poems of Music and the Dance, Poems of Emily Dickinson,* and *The Earth Is the Lord's: Poems of the Spirit*—have won her the respect and admiration of countless educators, librarians, and parents.

Mrs. Plotz was born in New York City and received an A.B. degree from Vassar College. For many years, she has served on the Children's Book Committee of the Child Study Association of America. She has taught children's literature at St. Joseph's College. Mrs. Plotz and her family consider travel their favorite hobby, and they have explored the United States and Europe several times. Mrs. Plotz lives in Brooklyn, New York.

ABOUT THE ARTIST

Ismar David was born in Breslau, Germany. He attended the Municipal Arts and Crafts School in Berlin where he studied decorative painting and graphic arts. Now an instructor of lettering and calligraphy, he also finds time for frequent trips to Europe and Israel. Mr. David and his wife live in New York City.